# RECR**ea**TION

### REALIZING THE EXTRAORDINARY CONTRIBUTION
### OF YOUR ENTERPRISE ARCHITECTS

## CHRIS POTTS

FRU**IT**ION TWO

# RECR**EA**TION

REALIZING THE EXTRAORDINARY CONTRIBUTION
OF YOUR ENTERPRISE ARCHITECTS

## CHRIS POTTS

# Technics Publications

New Jersey

Published by:
**Technics Publications, LLC**
Post Office Box 161
Bradley Beach, NJ 07720
www.technicspub.com

Edited by Carol Lehn
Cover design by Mark Brye

Copyright © 2010 by Technics Publications, LLC
Diagrams copyright Dominic Barrow Services Limited
Photographs copyright Chris Potts

ISBN, print ed.          978-1-9355040-8-5
ISBN, ePub ed.           978-1-9355043-7-5
ISBN, Kindle ed.         978-1-9355043-8-2

First Printing 2010
Library of Congress Control Number: 2010934005

*To Steve*

*…without whom 'fruITion' would still*

*be sitting quietly, unfinished, on a hard drive.*

# Contents

# Preface

Who, in truth, are the architects of your enterprise? And, where are these innovative, constructive people, who know how to combine aesthetics, structures, spaces and resources to produce an enterprise that is a statement to society, to other enterprises and to the world - unique, seductive and high-performing?

Most importantly, whoever and wherever your enterprise's architects are, what influence are they having on its shape and structure, and on the results of your strategies and business plans? For, being imaginative, creative people, they need to be having as much positive influence as possible, both individually and together, applying in practice consistent design themes and performance objectives.

Their contributions may be stunning innovations, or careful re-crafting of previous successes. Either way, they have the potential to make an extraordinary difference. The challenge for your enterprise is how best to realize this potential.

Step up Simon Rathbone, Enterprise Architect, to explore these questions. If you've read 'fruITion', you'll have met him already – and if not, no problem. He's going to describe what happened when he joined a global company based in New York, USA, as their first ever Vice President of Enterprise Architecture.

We catch up with Simon on a sunny Monday morning in Spring, as he walks into his new office and role. He will be working for the Chief Technology Officer, Lucy, who is also new to her role. Her boss, the Chief Executive Officer, likes to meet every new Vice President based in Corporate Headquarters as soon as they join the company.

Simon knows his subject, Enterprise Architecture, with all its frameworks, methods and tools, like the back of his hand. He knows how valuable it, and he, should be to the people who make the big decisions. Now he is going to meet the CEO on Day One, and can't wait to start the education process.

At the end of each chapter, I've made some observations about what Simon has told us. I encourage you to make your own observations - I expect you'll notice many different things from me.

# REVELATIONS

# ONE
# New York City, USA

I wasn't expecting the Chief Executive to say that we had the same job.

Well, you wouldn't, would you?

He didn't get it, obviously, which was to be expected, of course. I found it both frustrating and strangely reassuring that I could relocate nearly three-and-a-half thousand miles from London to New York and, again, find myself working for a CEO that didn't get Enterprise Architecture (or "EA", to you and me).

My new boss, Lucy, had told me in my final interview that Michael, the global CEO, would want to see me on my first day. She said that he always wanted to have a get-to-know-you conversation with every new member of the staff, from Vice President level upwards; just a short informal discussion, to help me bond with my new workplace, or something like that. Lucy and I had even role-played what I would say to him if I got the job.

Lucy, herself, had recently been promoted to Senior Vice President & Chief Technology Officer (CTO), and I was her new VP of EA. "Michael's very hands-on," she warned me, although she made it sound like a compliment.

Actually, when I met him, I immediately considered him to be rather distant. On arriving at his office, I announced myself to his Personal Assistant. She introduced herself as Trudy and said I must be the new English guy.

Guy? Something I would need to get used to, I supposed.

Trudy instructed me to go on in and take a seat at Michael's meeting table, then said that he had a call to Tokyo in five minutes' time. As I walked in, he was sitting at his desk behind a computer screen, humming to himself. Without looking up he said, "Never enough hours in the day." As it wasn't a question, and I wasn't even sure whether he knew I had come in, I didn't answer. Then he said, "You've got to be where the work is."

I still wasn't entirely certain whether he was talking to me or to himself. I thought the best thing to do was to take a chance and reply.

"Absolutely. You're right. Couldn't agree more."

He looked up, appearing a little surprised, rose from his seat, came over and sat down at the table. He took the chair next to me and placed it sideways to the table, and as he sat he stretched out his feet so that they almost directly pointed out the office door.

"Excellent. So what's your work, Simon? What do you do?"

"Enterprise Architecture."

He seemed to take a few moments to consider what I'd said, before he replied.

"Me too. Sounds like you and I have the same job. I expect we'll be seeing a lot of each other, then."

"Ok." I replied (thinking, "What?").

"Ok. Well, see you around." With a tough-looking smile and a handshake to match, he stood up and I did too, as he guided me towards the door. "Thank you for your time. Got to call Japan. Let's get together again real soon."

And that was the end of our meeting. Not how I would have done it, in Michael's position, but each to his own, I suppose.

"Lunch?" Lucy asked.

"I'm not sure I've got time. I want to get things off to a flying start, see what EA frameworks you're using, and what models and roadmaps you've got, if any."

"Make time. Come out to lunch with me."

Lucy was different from other managers that I'd worked with. For a start, she 'got' EA. Recently promoted to CTO from VP of IT[1] Service Delivery, and very ambitious, she had clearly spotted me as a like-

---

[1] Information Technology

minded person in our interviews. I knew we were going to get along just fine.

Down the street from the company's office in Manhattan is one of those excellent and very American places which is both a café and a deli, with hot food to go and a small convenience store. It has a mezzanine floor with tables and seating, so we ordered, paid, walked upstairs and sat down. From where we were, we could observe people coming and going below, shopping and ordering their lunches.

Lucy opened the conversation. "Well then, how did it go with Michael?"

"I was only with him for five minutes, at the most. He said that he and I must have the same job."

"But he's the Chief Executive."

"I know. I don't think he got it."

"That's been the trouble all along. Welcome to the show. Did you ask him what he meant?"

"No, because he had a call scheduled to Tokyo. He did remember my name, though, which my old CEO always failed to do."

"Tell me some more about your old CEO. What happened there?"

"She...."

"She?"

"Yes, Juliette. She didn't have a clue about IT or EA, but suddenly decided she knew all about IT strategy. She made all sorts of weird decisions, and in an unseemly rush. The CIO, Ian, didn't even try to stop her. I told him she was wrong, but he wouldn't listen."

I expected Lucy to say something at this stage, but she didn't. So I carried on, telling her about how Ian had given EA to Corporate Strategy without even a fight. I mean, what would they know about EA? Lucy asked me what I thought would happen there next. I said that it was too soon to tell, but I was sure it would all turn out to be very temporary and EA would be back home in IT before long, once Corporate Strategy found out how little they knew about it.

"Why didn't you hang around, then?"

"I care too much about EA, I suppose, to put up with people who don't know anything about it making such big mistakes. Who knows what kind of mess they would make of it before giving it back? Anyway, I'm really pleased to be over here now."

"It's good to have you. We need to sort out our global IT infrastructure. It contains a lot of redundancy, fragmentation and replication. I know you're the man to do it."

"Thank you."

"You're welcome."

The next morning, I turned up early for work, but Lucy was already there.

"Breakfast," she said, and we went out for coffee and Danish.

"I need you to go to Toronto, tomorrow. Get to know the main architecture guys up there and see what you think we need to do. My assistant, Warren, will give you the details and book everything. Just tell him what you need. Report back to me by the end of the day on Thursday."

"Next Thursday?"

"No, the day after tomorrow. Stay over and spend some time with them, then get the first flight back on Thursday and drop me an email report as soon as you can."

"OK." Talk about hitting the ground running!

I asked her who I would be meeting. She said I should focus on two people, Ivan and Frankie. They were the movers-and-shakers in EA up there. If I needed to influence anyone, it would be them.

It was time to start sorting out the world, then, starting with Toronto.

## Observations

- What people hear in the words 'Enterprise Architecture' depends on the audience.

- Hold a debrief after any meeting with the CEO about the enterprise's architecture.

- Enterprise Architecture in the context of corporate strategy is very different from EA in the context of IT.

- While architecture must take account of infrastructure, this is unlikely to be the best place for Enterprise Architecture to start.

- Enterprise Architecture is founded on collaboration and influence.

# TWO
# Toronto, Canada

Ivan and Frankie were really polite. I'd expected them both to be men, but Frankie turned out to be a woman whose real name is Françoise!

However, as soon as I started talking through their work with them, I didn't think they really wanted me to be there. They were a bit threatened, I thought, by the breadth and depth of my EA knowledge and experience.

We talked through their architecture and where they were taking it. They showed me their 'as is' and 'to be' architecture models and the roadmap from one to the other. The 'as is' model was the usual spaghetti, although better than some I'd seen. Their 'to be' model, and roadmap for getting there, were really quite elegant. I asked them what the main issues were with achieving the roadmap. Their answer was as I expected: the company executives. True to form, their local management hadn't yet understood the importance of having a robust and agile architecture. Making a business case for some of the developments in the roadmap was proving to be both a practical and political challenge. It was hard to put numbers on the investments and the business benefits in a way that satisfied Finance, but it was the executives' reluctance to back architectural investments that was the most significant risk to the roadmap's success. The Canadians asked me what solution I would recommend. I was able to reassure them that many organizations were suffering from the same problems, and that better EA governance was likely to be the answer.

Which led us to wonder out loud how on earth companies had ever managed before they had Enterprise Architects?

After work, Frankie and Ivan took me out for drinks and dinner via the CN Tower, as I'd never been to Toronto before – or, indeed, anywhere in Canada. The ascent up the tower was unnerving, because the elevators are on the outside and made of glass, which means you can see out all the way up to the observation deck. I'm not especially afraid of heights, but as the comforting activity of the city receded below, I felt increasingly in another, unreal world. At risk of sounding strange, the more of the city I saw, the less I could discern its shape. It really looked nothing like the map that I had. From the main observation deck, we took a second elevator to the Skypod, which announced itself to be 147 floors up (a bit odd, to my mind, because the CN Tower has no floors). Although we were obviously much higher than before, there was some point at which more height didn't seem to make the city, way below, look any different.

It was while we were way up there in the Skypod that I received an email from Lucy. Isn't technology fantastic, I thought. Here is her email, in its entirety:

```
Simon,

How's Toronto? Michael wants to
see you on Thursday afternoon.
Be at my office at 4:45 P.M.

Lucy
```

I asked my Canadian colleagues why they thought Michael might want to see me. They asked me who Michael was, so I told them he was the company's global CEO. They looked at each other, then back at me, said nothing more on the subject and suggested we go back down into the city.

We went to a bar that they knew, somewhere quite close by. They probably found me a little distracted because of Lucy's email. How was I going to have enough time both to summarize for her my visit to Toronto, and to get ready for whatever Michael wanted? Did Michael also want to know what I thought of the Canadian's EA roadmap? He had said that we were both doing the same job, so maybe he was another Enterprise Architect who had made it all the way up to CEO, a possibility that I hadn't considered. That seemed very unlikely, but I had no idea what his actual background was. Perhaps he was a former CTO, or another CEO - like my previous one - who thought he knew something about IT.

Frankie bought us all a beer and asked what Michael was like. I could only tell her about my short meeting with him and repeat Lucy's warning that he was 'really hands-on'. It turned out Frankie really wanted to know what he looked like. Using Ivan's phone we found a picture of him on the company's website, looking a little younger than when I met him. Frankie studied the picture for a few seconds and, without looking up, said, "You're much better looking than him."

I was stunned.

I looked at Ivan and he winked. Winked! So far all of our work and socializing had remained totally professional. Frankie was, in my mind, the same as Ivan and me, a professional Enterprise Architect.

I quickly decided to ignore the implications of Frankie's comment and Ivan's inappropriate wink by going quiet and concentrating on my beer. After a while, I asked where we were going for dinner.

"We like the Hard Rock Café," said Ivan, "Is that OK?"

I said it had been a long time since I'd been to one, but that it was fine.

Ivan continued, with something of a proud flourish, "It's just up Yonge Street – the longest street in the world!"

"According to vous Torontonians, that is." Frankie countered, slipping partly into French.

I asked Frankie where she was from, and she replied "Montréal".

"Is that a long way from here?"

"Only about 300 miles or so, but culturally, it's much further. It's the second largest French-speaking city in the world after Paris."

The Hard Rock Café was a fairly short walk from the bar. When we arrived, it immediately struck me as looking very different from the only other two I had been in, and said so.

"I thought all these places were based on the same standard design, but this one is really different from the others I've been to in London and Paris."

Frankie asked me what was different. I said the main difference was that the others seemed much darker, while the Toronto one was light. The London and Paris restaurants are in older buildings than this one looked, and seemed somehow separate from the world outside. The Toronto restaurant felt much more openly part of the wider city, with large windows overlooking the neighboring square, and tables outside.

"You should try the one in New York, then," said Ivan, "That's underground."

Over dinner, I told them that my older brother had taken me to the very first of their restaurants, in London, while I was still a teenager. Frankie said that Lucy was 'completely nuts' about Hard Rock Cafés and visited them wherever she went. She had an encyclopedic knowledge of where they all were, what they all looked like and the rock memorabilia they had on the walls.

"Tell her you saw Bob Dylan's guitar," Frankie said excitedly.

"Which one's that?"

"The acoustic one over there."

"Oh." It looked much like an ordinary guitar to me.

Apparently reading my thoughts, Frankie said, "Who would have believed someone could use such simple technology to make so much wonderful poetry and music."

"And money." I said, to which Ivan frowned.

Over dinner we talked some more about music, although it isn't really my best subject. When we had finished I went back to my hotel, slept, woke up and caught the first plane back to New York.

## Observations

- Executives may not appreciate, or agree with, the value of architectural investments.

- A diagram of something (e.g. a map) often bears little resemblance to reality (e.g. a city).

- Applying standard design themes is very different from having standard designs.

- Good design will take account of the surrounding environment.

- Technology has no enterprise; someone with enterprise can create value from technology.

# THREE
## New York City, USA

Back in the New York office on Thursday morning, I wrote a summary of my Toronto visit for Lucy and emailed it to her. She immediately replied with a thank-you email and promised to talk to me later, when she had read it.

At 4:45 P.M., I went to Lucy's office as instructed, ahead of the meeting with Michael. I had not prepared anything, as I had no idea why he had asked to see me again.

"What have you got for Michael?" asked Lucy.

I trusted her enough to admit that I had nothing, as nobody had informed me of the meeting's objective. As I said it, I realized that I could have asked for the objective, or even drafted one myself. For a moment I was nervous that she would be expecting me to have something ready, so I was equally relieved when Lucy said that she didn't know what Michael wanted, either.

"Let's go," she said, and headed for the elevator.

As we arrived at Michael's office, Trudy, the PA, said, "Go straight in."

"Hey, Lucy! Simon!" Michael was already waiting at his table for us and seemed to be in a good mood. As soon as we sat down, he looked straight at me and said, "You're coming to Tokyo with me."

Before I could stop myself, I replied, "Why?"

"Great question!" Was he being straight or sarcastic? "Because the new President of our subsidiary over there thinks he's got a problem with their structural performance, and wants some help from us to verify what it is and figure out the answer. I was due to go and see him anyway, and now that you're here, I reckoned you would want to come too. Structural performance is right up your alley."

"When are you going?"

"We're going on Saturday, and I'm coming back on Wednesday. You can stay as long as you need to. Just tell Trudy what you need and she'll book everything for us. Meet me in the airport lounge at JFK, and we can do some planning on the way. Any questions?"

I couldn't think of any questions and Lucy said nothing, so I said I would see Michael on Saturday. We headed back to the elevator, and to the relative safety of Lucy's office.

Lucy asked me, "What did he mean by 'structural performance'?"

"I don't know, but he clearly expects me to. 'Right up my alley', he said. There's something not right about this. How come I'm going to Tokyo with the global Chief Executive, to work with the local President? I'm only the Enterprise Architect."

"Well said, my friend. We need a drink."

We left the office and headed for a bar that Lucy knew, a couple of blocks away. She bought us both a beer, and we sat at a corner table where we could talk.

The first thing she did was to ask me what I had found in Toronto, as she hadn't had a chance to read my email. When I told her that it all looked quite good up there, although they did need to improve their EA governance, she looked a little concerned but said nothing. Instead of talking any more about the architecture, she asked me about Ivan and Frankie. I told her, with some embarrassment, that I had expected Frankie to be a man. Lucy said that she - Frankie - was a bit of a complicated character and, based on the feedback Lucy had already sought from Ivan, I had done well to get along with her as well as I did.

"Did she start flirting with you?" Lucy asked, very directly.

I said that I thought so, but I had tried to ignore it.

"Best way to deal with it. Trouble is, you're a good-looking guy, and Frankie wants a man."

Clearly, I must have blushed enough for Lucy to notice, even in the subdued light of the bar.

"You English guys embarrass easily, it seems."

I didn't know Lucy well enough, yet, to tell her that I didn't think I was a 'good-looking guy', nor was I used to women saying that I was. I grew up believing the school-yard taunts and buried myself in my studies.

Instead, I told her we had eaten at the Hard Rock Café.

"Great, aren't they? Did you see Bob Dylan's guitar?"

"Yes I did," I answered, privately thanking Ivan for the prompt.

"The one in Tokyo is in Roppongi. I've never been there. See if you can get there and tell me what it's like. Anyway, drink up, then let's have another beer and get back to why Michael wants you to go with him."

Lucy was a faster drinker than I was, but I thought I had better try to keep up and bought the second round of beers.

"So, what did Frankie actually say to you?"

"I thought we were going to talk about Michael."

"Oh, yes. Michael. Structural performance." And with that, to my further embarrassment, Lucy, the global CTO, started giggling.

I asked her what was so funny.

She straightened her face and said, "Absolutely nothing." and then started giggling again. "Come on, Simon, lighten up!"

I said that I was sorry, but I still didn't know what she was finding funny.

After she had calmed down, she put her hand on my shoulder and told me that she didn't know what Michael wanted with his structural performance thingy (that's what she said), but he would expect me to be entertaining company. He was a ruthless businessman, to say the least, but enjoyed having a good time with his people, when he got the chance. What's more, if he liked working with someone, he would draw them very close to him.

She changed the subject and asked me, "So, what do you think of our beautiful city?"

I told her it was very impressive.

"Is that it? Impressive? Come on! You're talking to someone who is in love with this place - the people, the streets, the buildings, the spaces. Do you know that each time you walk from one block to the next, you may as well be in a different town? I bet there's no other city on Earth so diverse. You must at least like the architecture, being an Enterprise Architect."

"Yes, I suppose I do; what I've seen of it so far."

"Which is your favorite building?"

"I don't think I have one, yet. I have only just arrived, after all. Which one do you like best?"

"I'm a Chrysler girl. Been in love with it since I was little." The she suddenly stood up and said, "Back in a minute."

And she was, with two more beers, although I hadn't half-finished the previous one yet, and nor had she.

She pushed my half-empty glass towards me and picked up hers. "Race you to the bottom. England versus America. On three." I picked up mine, too. "One, two,..."

"Hold on, is that drink on three, or three and then drink?"

"Three and then drink. One, two, three."

I think she let me win.

"Now the big one," she said, and pushed the full glass towards me.

I asked her if she was joking, but she just picked up her glass and I really had to do the same. "One, two, three," and down it went. This time she won. I didn't even quite manage to drink all of mine. As I put the glass down, I slammed it hard into the table top and the remaining beer exploded out the top.

"Oops." I said. "Oopsy-oops."

"In case you hadn't noticed, Mr. Simon-impressive-structural-performance-Rathbone, I am getting you drunk. Bet Frankie didn't manage that!"

"Me? Drunk? I don't think so, Miss Lucy-Chryslergirl-Hau." I was so pleased with myself for this quick-fire response that I rocked backwards on my chair and it started to tip over. Luckily there was a wall behind and it stopped at about thirty degrees from the vertical, so I just stayed like that thinking that it was a rather entertaining position.

"Actually, it's Mrs. Chryslergirl-Hau."

"Oh. Sorry."

"Just joking. Got you there. You've gone all red, again."

I realized that quite a few people in the bar were looking at me, and thought I had better get my chair back into its normal position. But I couldn't, because it was just at the angle where it seemed I couldn't rock it forward and when I grabbed hold of the table, it was the table that moved not the chair. Lucy eventually offered me her hand, and pulled both me and my chair forward far enough for it to tip back into place.

She turned to her audience and announced, quite fondly, "It's OK, folks, he's new here. And he's from England." After that, some of the people watching found a moment to come over and talk to me. Was I new to America, or just New York? How long had I been here? Did I have everything I needed? I don't think I managed many coherent answers, but I was impressed by their friendliness.

"OK," said Lucy, "One more beer then we'd better do the serious stuff."

I thought that another beer would leave me incapable of doing anything, serious or otherwise, but she disappeared off to buy them before I could say anything. In fact, we did Lucy's serious stuff with surprising lucidity (a good word to use when you're drunk with Lucy), keeping the two last beers at hand, but neither of us finishing them.

She became quite intense, all of a sudden. "Some more about Michael. I think I told you already that he's a ruthless businessman, and he needs to be. That is also how he will expect you to be. He's turned this company around in the last couple of years, and now wants us to innovate and grow, big time. Before he became CEO, he was the global SVP of Brands and Marketing. The previous CEO was all about efficiency, so we made money by saving money, in effect. Michael is swinging the pendulum the other way. He wants us to be more productive, not just more efficient. Personally, he is quite forgiving, but professionally, he is not. He will help you if he sees that you're working towards his agenda, but if he thinks for one moment that you're not, then, well, none of us will be able to save you. So if you're unsure of something he wants you to do, tell him. He may raise his voice at you, but that's almost certainly for effect. He will expect you to give as good as you get. Any questions?"

I didn't know if I wanted to go to Tokyo with Michael, but I supposed I had no choice. I sat silently looking at the people in the bar and, for want of something to do, took a sip of my beer. I did, in the end, think of a question.

"What if he gets me drunk, like this?"

"Enjoy yourself, but stay in control at all times. Try not to call him any funny names."

With that last comment, I thought that Lucy was lightening the atmosphere again.

"You started it."

"Yes, but provoked would be a better word."

"You did all this on purpose?"

"I think you are going to be brilliant, but you have some issues that I knew I needed to work on as soon as Michael told you to go with him."

"What issues?"

"Don't worry, we all do. I can see you are looking concerned, even if I am nearly four beers to the good." She lifted her glass, and declared, "To Tokyo."

## Observations

- Structural performance is a key indicator of an enterprise's architectural wellbeing.

- Enterprise Architects must expect to be working with senior executives.

- How interested in other forms of architecture should people working in Enterprise Architecture be?

- Self-awareness and personal relationships are fundamental to success as an Enterprise Architect.

# FOUR
## Travelling to Tokyo

On Saturday, I went to JFK airport to meet Michael in the lounge. I was surprised to find that we were travelling on a Japanese airline, rather than an American one. I asked him why and he replied that he liked to remind himself of the culture of the country he was visiting, before he got there.

"That's why I have a real issue with codeshare flights," he said. "Airlines seem proud of their Brands, yet will readily book you on a flight that's in their name then hand you over to another company. The fact that many of the airlines are flag-carriers for their countries just makes it worse. Today we could have had Trudy book a Japanese flight that is actually on an

American airline, and vice versa. I think you've got to visibly value your Brands and Service more than that. Let's face it, if you don't, who will?"

"I see what you mean," I said, although I knew a few people working for airlines who would see it very differently.

"Good. Let's get a drink and talk about enterprise architecture." From his tone of voice, I could tell that he hadn't capitalized those last two words. Also, mindful of Lucy's warning, I waited to see what Michael had to drink before choosing mine. It was lucky I did, as he simply got a mineral water, so I chose a Coke.

When we were both sitting down, he continued. "I thought I would do some research, after our conversation on Monday. I didn't realize there was something officially called Enterprise Architecture, I just thought you'd come up with a neat way of describing what we executives do. So it's mainly to do with IT, is that right?"

"Yes. No. Well, at least that's where it started. But it's becoming much more about the business."

"Good, because I know about business. So, are you just an IT guy? That explains why you're working for Lucy."

"No, I'm not just an IT guy."

"What else are you, then?"

"These days, I like to think of myself as more of a process guy."

Quick as a flash, Michael said, "OK, here's my process principle, then. The customer has the process. We have to decide how we want to appear in that process - what we want to contribute to the customer's experience - and make sure that's what our day-to-day performance actually achieves. How am I doing?"

"That's a bit different from the model I've always been taught. Can I think about it for a moment?"

"Sure, take your time." He stood up and walked off.

When he came back, he seemed to have forgotten about processes and talked of Lucy. "Lucy has the potential to be a brilliant leader, which is why I made her CTO. I want her to outgrow that role as quickly as she can. What do you think of her, so far?"

I told him that I was uncomfortable with talking about my manager in her absence. His answer was one I had not predicted, and I have to admit it scared me a lot.

"OK, I understand. I admire your integrity. So from now on, you work for me. With what I have in mind for our company, two enterprise architects won't be enough, but at least we have each other until we can find some more. So, now what do you think of Lucy? Will she make a great leader, or not?"

"Yes, she will. In fact, given my short time working at your company, I think she already is."

"Our company."

"Sorry, our company."

"If you ever say 'your company' again, I'll fire you."

Again, I wasn't sure whether he was joking or not. He certainly had no trace of humor on his face.

He continued, "I think she may be a great departmental leader, but that's not what we need. She needs to show much more leadership to the entire company. Like you and I have to do. We'll see if she sticks to leading the technology operation or is more enterprising than that. Anyway, you were telling me what you thought."

I picked up the word 'enterprising' in his assessment of Lucy, and assumed he'd placed it there on purpose. Smart!

"Yes, that's likely to be her biggest challenge. To get out of the technology silo and provide leadership to our company around the world. On a personal level, I've found her to be both sharp and wise – I mean sharp in intellect, not cutting."

"Good observation. Because she needs to be more cutting sometimes, show people like me a bit less respect."

Then, all of a sudden, he changed the subject back to processes and asked me what I thought of his principle.

"Like I said," I replied, "It's a bit different from the model I was taught, which is, in effect, the other way up. In that model, customers appear in our processes, not us in theirs. And, similarly, in the model I'm used to, we create experiences for customers, rather than contribute to experiences they are already having. What do you see as a customer's process, if you don't mind me asking?"

"I don't mind at all. You can ask me anything you like. Here are some examples: going on a business trip, or a vacation; having a baby; moving home; changing job; buying a new car; etc. Based on what you just said, it's no wonder we struggle to meet our Brand promise, and it explains why our people keep on about things like 'the sales process'."

"But we do have processes that don't involve customers."

"Such as?"

"Strategy, and planning, for example."

"True, and making investments. So let's talk about our business in Tokyo. Have you got the numbers with you?"

Which numbers? "Which numbers?"

"Japan's performance numbers. Here. You can borrow mine." He reached for his briefcase, which was on the floor by his chair, took out a single sheet of paper and handed it to me. On it was a table of numbers and some handwritten notes. As I started to try and make sense of it, he said, "Revenues rising, profits rising, structural performance in decline. I think you'll find the two ratios I've been looking at especially interesting." He was pointing to his handwritten notes and I could see 'revenues per dollar of operating cost!' and 'profit per completed transaction!' I asked him if I could borrow the numbers and do some thinking. "No problem. Be my guest. Look at the shape of the numbers, not the actual figures," he said, effectively ending our conversation.

And it was time to board the plane, so I put the sheet with the numbers on it into my backpack.

We found our seats, settled into them and the cabin crew gave us complimentary champagne. Michael held his up for a toast: "to enterprise architecture". So there I was, with the global CEO of my new company, in the first class cabin of a Japanese aeroplane, on the way to Tokyo to sort out their structural performance, toasting 'enterprise architecture' - and wondering whether it was the anything like the Enterprise Architecture that I knew and loved.

The plane took off, climbed and leveled out. After they had served us a meal, I returned to Michaels' sheet of paper. Here are the numbers it contained:

**Headline Operating Results**

|  | Year 1 | Year 2 | Year 3 | Year 4 | Year 5 | Year 6 | Year 7 |
|---|---|---|---|---|---|---|---|
| Completed Transactions | 21.16 | 29.30 | 80.22 | 170.61 | 262.55 | 341.03 | 462.72 |
| Revenues | 24.3 | 26.3 | 75.6 | 141.0 | 196.5 | 232.8 | 339.5 |
| Operating Expenses | 24.8 | 26.4 | 70.7 | 127.9 | 177.0 | 213.5 | 315.4 |
| Profit | (0.5) | (0.1) | 4.9 | 13.1 | 19.5 | 19.3 | 24.1 |

*Completed Transactions in millions*
*Revenues, Operating Expenses and Profit in $millions*

Being a visual person, I decided the best thing to do was to put them into a spreadsheet, get it to calculate the ratios that Michael already seemed to know, and illustrate them as graphs:

# Structural Performance Ratios

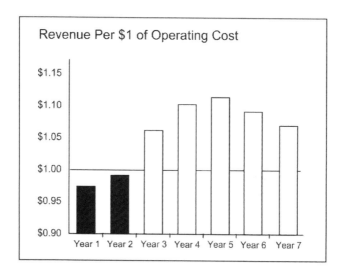

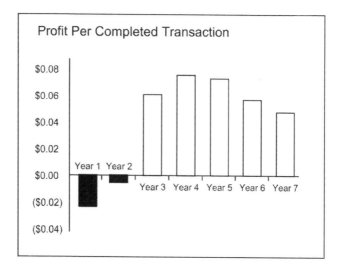

These graphs revealed what Michael and, I assumed, our company President in Japan, already knew. In recent years, both ratios showed that while Revenues and Profits were rising, our subsidiary's structural performance had started to decay. I also noticed that Michael's ratios were focused on productivity, not efficiency. They were about how much the enterprise produced from a unit of investment (such as the Revenue from each dollar invested in Operating Expenses), rather than how little resource it invested for a unit of production. That reminded me of what Lucy had told me about the difference between Michael's strategy and that of his predecessor. Depending on which way you treated the same underlying ratio (as productivity or efficiency), I was beginning to see how the actual behaviors of the enterprise would be very different.

Did Michael and the President think I would know what to do about the decline in structural performance? For a start, how was I supposed to know the reason why it was happening?

I think I went into a kind of daydream for a while, then plucked up enough courage to go back and see Michael. I showed him the numbers and graphs on my laptop.

"Good," he said, "Now we're on the same page."

"Why are their structural ratios decaying?"

"That's for them to say, not us. We are, after all, the investors in their business; their only investors, in fact. And as the investors, we have to ask them to account for the decline in their performance. If we agree with their reasons, we can certainly help them decide what to do differently. And, if we're confident in their strategies and plans for turning it around, we may also invest some more of our capital in them. To borrow the first part of your job title, we'll want to know that they have the enterprise to go with our capital, to choose some good structural innovations that result in better, more productive performance."

"Just about every business I've ever worked in treated the people from Head Office, like us, as an overhead, not their investors."

"That's the fault of the people in the Head Office, then. It sounds like they need to sort out their own place in the enterprise's architecture before they try and help anyone else. Perhaps people are confusing the corporation's strategic role as investor with its operational role of managing capabilities that are shared between its businesses. In any case, be in no doubt, we are the investors, not an overhead, and I expect you to think and act like one at all times."

"Ok."

Besides being another of the scariest moments in my career, this conversation was also one of the most liberating. What would it be like, as an Enterprise Architect, to think and act like one of the investors in our businesses, rather than as an overhead?

## Observations

- From the perspective of your customers, their experiences with your Brands and Service equals your enterprise's architecture.

- An executive who researches the scope of EA is likely to conclude that it is centered on IT.

- The customer has the process. To design your enterprise's architecture, start by deciding which of your customer's processes and experiences you want to appear in, and how you want to appear.

- The structural performance of an enterprise's architecture is measured using ratios.

- Enterprise Architects represent the interests of the investor.

In Tokyo, I was Bill Murray.

Not literally, of course, but I felt like how Bill's character appeared to feel in the movie 'Lost in Translation' - culturally apart, not able to find a way in. Michael and I even stayed in the hotel that the movie was set in, the Park Hyatt in the Shinjuku district of the city. At night, the view from the hotel bar on the $52^{nd}$ floor was extraordinary (the bar is called the New York Bar, which seemed apt, as that was where we had just come from). Looking out and down, there were uncountable numbers of soft, red lights flashing on the tops of the buildings. The experience of simply sitting and looking out at them was a feeling of peace.

Over a beer in the bar, Michael and I talked about Japan's numbers and what to do with them. In truth, Michael talked and I listened. I was getting lost in more than just the Japanese culture. His approach, which he had hinted at already, was that as the investors we would ask the new President of our Japanese business to tell us what he was planning to do about the fact that structural performance had peaked and was now in decline. We would be supportive, but not rescuing. We were not there to tell the President and his team the answer. Part of Michael's design for the architecture of the worldwide company, he said, was to give people the structure and space to exploit their own enterprise. We would keep a hold on the context, such as the integrity of our Brands and Service, the need to see a return on our investment, and to ensure legal and regulatory compliance. Within this framework, we would offer encouragement and guidance where that would help to enhance people's success.

"I expect you've worked with some CEOs who prefer a much more directive, constraining architecture. More structure, less space," he said. Then he asked me, "What would you like to hear from the President?"

Michael had clearly done to me what he said he had in mind for the company. He had established a context (his principle that The Customer Has the Process, and architectural performance) with some structure (the ratios and our roles as investors) and now an enormous space with encouragement and guidance for me to exploit my own enterprise.

But the space I now found myself in was not anything like the ones I was familiar and comfortable with. Lost in Translation had rapidly become Lost in Space.

Remembering Lucy's advice, I admitted to Michael that this was not the Enterprise Architecture I was used to. I did not have an answer to his question about what to ask the President.

"OK. I'll give you a choice. Come with me to meet the President, or go and see the people in IT and show them the ratios. See what they make of them."

I sensed a trap, if only of my own making, which was the option to return there-and-then to IT architecture. I also wondered whether the people in IT would feel they were in a position to influence the ratios, other than by restructuring the IT that the company used or by getting it delivered more efficiently. "I'd like to do both, but my preference is to see the President. However, I may not have much to say."

"Play it by ear. Sit with me in my meeting with the President, and see what comes to mind."

It seemed we had finished, but Michael said he was going out for a walk before retiring for the night. "Come with me," he said.

So we left the hotel and walked up the street to the main area of Shinjuku, which is full of the neon signs, busy streets and people that Tokyo is so famous for. "Take a look at this," Michael said, and headed down some narrow side streets on which there were tiny bars, examples of much older, traditional buildings than the surrounding district. Each bar looked like it could hold about ten customers, at the most. He chose one, in particular, and went in. Everyone else in there was Japanese. The man behind the bar said, in a perfect English accent, "Hello, Michael-san. It's good to see you again. Suntory Whiskey?"

"Make that two. I would like to introduce my friend, Simon-san."

"Good to meet you. You are welcome." said the barman.

"Thank you," I replied.

"Arigato," Michael said to me, "Japanese for thank you." And after a short pause, he concluded, "Now, this is what I call a bar. The hotel is great, but for me, this is the true Tokyo experience."

The next morning we met with the President of our Japanese business, in his office in the Shiodome district of Tokyo. Michael and he started by exchanging small gifts. The President gave me one also, but I did not have one to offer in return.

"Is this your first time here?" he asked and I said that it was. I privately reflected on how many different first times I was experiencing, at that moment.

"How are you finding it?"

"There is much to experience and learn."

Michael and the President made themselves comfortable, and started their meeting. The tone of the discussion was one of negotiation. I saw Michael act as the investor, just as he said he would, requiring the President to state how he was going to improve the fall-off in structural performance that the ratios were indicating. The President responded that they would be likely to need an injection of capital from the global corporation, and some hands-on assistance. He also said that he would be concerned if they were expected to invest in too much 'future value' at the expense of continuing to return year-on-year growth in revenues and profits. Michael tacitly acknowledged the request for investment without directly answering one way or the other. I was, I assumed, supposed to represent some of the hands-on assistance.

Michael took the discussion into a new and specific topic. "One of the structural changes that I'm thinking of making to the corporation is to consolidate, into one or more hubs, capabilities that are common to some, or all, of our businesses."

The President replied, "Yes, that's a tactic I have seen before, and the hubs are usually called 'shared services organizations'. They have their advantages, but I have also experienced the issues that having them can cause. I also think it would require a very big change in our company's culture to take full advantage of the new structure."

"Please tell me about the issues you have seen," Michael replied.

"Behavioral ones, between the people in the hubs and us in the businesses. They can seem to forget that we are all part of the same corporation - that our customers are equally their customers; and we struggle to gain their empathy."

I suddenly thought of something to say!

"Do you mind if I suggest an alternative?" I asked both of them at once.

Michael said, frowning slightly, "Sure, be our guest."

With both the President and Michael now silent and looking at me, I asked, "I think it might be worth exploring whether or not we could achieve the benefits of hubs without them actually needing to exist."

Neither of them said anything in reply, but as I made to speak again (although I did not know what I was actually going to say), Michael held up his hand for me to stay quiet. Eventually the President said, "Virtual hubs. Fascinating. How would they work?"

Michael replied, "I will commission someone to find out." Which was lucky, as I had no idea. Of the President, he asked "Will you help us with that work?" to which the President nodded. To me, Michael said. "Thank you, Simon. That's very innovative."

The President and Michael returned to their negotiations, which concluded with agreement from Michael to make investment available to the Japanese business, subject to a robust strategy and business plan. The President said he was delighted with this outcome and everyone parted on friendly terms.

Afterwards, back in the New York Bar, Michael said to me, "You took a huge risk there, but it paid off."

I was not aware that I had taken a risk, although I had noticed his frown when I asked to say something.

He continued, "I expected you to clear with me, beforehand, anything that you were going to propose. You didn't. Fortunately, your intervention was a good one, as the negotiations were beginning to go nowhere. But never do that again."

"I'm sorry, Michael, but you told me to say whatever came to mind."

"That's not quite what I said. But, no apologies, no regrets. Make that your professional foundation. Now I have something I want you to do for me. I think you are going to like it."

"Does this have anything to do with the virtual hubs?"

"No, although I'll get whomever I commission to look at that idea to come to you for guidance. If they don't, I expect you to track them down and make sure that they do."

"OK."

Michael then told me what he wanted me to do. In fact, he chose these words very carefully. Starting with the outcome, he said that we needed to get people growing the performance of our businesses with what he called structural innovations. Creating much more value, he said, by discovering, investing in, and exploiting new ideas for the shape and structure of each business, and of the corporation as a whole. "I want you to visit some more of our businesses in different countries. Explore their structural performance with them and help them to express their ideas on how to enhance it by investing in innovative change. Add some more ideas of your own, if you like, but mainly you are to act as facilitator. What I really want back from you is a repeatable process, a journey that people can follow to do this everywhere, including back in New York. We need to unlock the magic that I believe is out there in people who can think and act architecturally, like you and me. Let's find the other enterprise architects, wherever they are, and create a network of value-creating innovators."

## Observations

- A corporate-level Enterprise Architect who personally designs an individual business unit risks a significant conflict of interests.

- The balance between space and structure in an enterprise's architecture depends on the style of business leadership.

- There is value in old architecture, as well as new architecture.

- An appreciation of local culture is vital for success as an Enterprise Architect.

- The relationships between the elements of an architecture make it more, or less, cohesive.

- The 'end game' of Enterprise Architecture is to become integral to mainstream business management.

# SIX

## Thin Air

Michael and I travelled back to New York together, although he had originally said I could stay longer if I wanted to. I never did go and see our IT people in Tokyo.

For the first few hours of the flight, while still in daylight, I could see through my window the darkening blue space above and a near-cloudless view of the sea below.

I asked him if I could take time out to think about what he had instructed me to do, and he said this was no problem at all. Although Lucy had said that he enjoyed people's company, I noticed how he seemed happy to be on his own, as well.

My problem was that I did not know where to start. A blank sheet of paper can be hard sometimes. But I knew that Michael wanted me to design the repeatable journey myself and verify it with colleagues in our businesses, rather than pull out one that someone else had already prepared.

Also, the more Michael expressed his confidence in me, the less I seemed to have. I began to wonder who I might turn to for support, independent of the people I was now working with, perhaps to give me the confidence I needed. The same person kept coming to mind. The trouble was that the last time we had spoken, I had been very angry with him. But before the situation that had caused all that we had been very close, and now I wanted to ask his advice. That person was my old CIO in London, Ian Taylor. I resolved to call him when we were back on the ground.

Meanwhile, up here in our communal metal tube that was hurtling at an extraordinary speed through a freezing sky, it was for me alone to decide how to approach the task that Michael had given me - where to start, where to end, and what to do in between.

There are times that I can best express myself by doodling while I am thinking, and this was one of those times. I started writing EA, and the words "Enterprise" and "Architecture" on my blank sheet of paper, in all sorts of different ways. I then wondered what words I could think of for my repeatable journey that started with E and A. From all of this emerged something tangible, although if you asked me how I found it, I would not be able to tell you for sure. As with many ideas, it just seemed to come out of thin air.

I would call my process "Double-E, Double-A", and it would be made up of four steps. For a moment, I had a complicated idea that I would call it "e(EA)a", signifying that it was about making formal Enterprise Architecture integral to informal enterprise architecture, but decided to keep it as simply EEAA. The four steps I chose were Establish - Explore - Activate - Apply, like this:

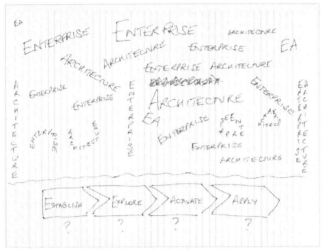

**Simon's EEAA Doodle**

Now, at least, I had more than a blank space with which to start my odyssey. I took my sketch of the EEAA journey to show Michael, but he was asleep; and snoring, I might add. Never mind. I would just continue to plan how I would do it and see what happened along the way.

## Observations

- Personal autonomy and self-expression are valuable characteristics in EA leadership.

- A blank piece of paper with no preconceptions can be a hard place to start, but may be necessary for innovation.

- The best ideas will sometimes come out of thin air, rather than from a pre-meditated thought process.

- Architecturally, designing the overall shape of something (e.g. Simon's process) is likely to come before designing its detailed structure.

# SEVEN
# Back in New York City, USA

Lucy wanted to know what the Hard Rock Café in Tokyo was like. I told her it was the same, but different, all over again. It was interesting to think that, all the way from Toronto to Tokyo, while each restaurant reflected something different about the community and building in which it was placed, there was also a great deal of familiarity in the experience. How do they do that? What's the secret? Lucy also said that she thought the people who ran that business were very entrepreneurial. It was intriguing to watch how, over time and around the world, they closed some restaurants and opened others.

**69**

I asked Lucy how she felt about me now reporting directly to Michael. She smiled and with the back of her hand she flicked her hair, which was long and dark, in a way that I realized I had seen her do before, although I didn't know what it meant. "I'm cool," she said, "Enjoy."

That seemed to be the end of that topic of conversation, so I then told her that I needed her help. "I'm going to go on a trip to visit some more of our businesses in different countries, to build up my knowledge about how things work out there, see what I can do to help them, and develop a repeatable journey for EA that Michael has asked me to do. Where do you think I should go?"

"How many countries?"

Thinking about my Double-E, Double-A journey, I replied, "Four".

She reflected quietly for a few moments, and then told me the places she thought I should go. "OK. Try these. Sydney in Australia, Hong Kong in China, Paris in France, and Abu Dhabi in the United Arab Emirates. And if you want a fifth, come back via Toronto."

"Why Toronto again? I was just there."

"I think you'll find it's different next time."

Michael had told me to ask his Personal
Assistant, Trudy, to help me with the travel
arrangements, so I took the elevator up to see her.

"Good", she said, as soon as I arrived in her
office, "Michael wants to see you. Go in."

I walked into his office on my own for the first
time since my initial 'welcome to the company'
meeting with him, which seemed like ages ago. It felt
like a very different space from then, but of course, it
was me that had changed. He was on the phone, and
instead of sitting at his meeting table I walked over to a
couple of chairs that he had in front of his desk. He
indicated that I should sit down.

"I've been thinking," he started, after ending his
call. "Until you walked in here the other day, I hadn't
thought of what I did as enterprise architecture. Now I
do. Thank you."

My own memory of that first meeting was that
I'd said it was me, not Michael, who was the Enterprise
Architect.

He continued, "How's the planning coming along? Have you decided where you're going?"

"I've chosen five places to visit, with Lucy's help. I was just about to ask Trudy to make the bookings."

"Which five places?"

I repeated the list that Lucy had recommended.

"Those places, in that order? Good. Give me a call if you need anything. Meanwhile I'll let each of our local Presidents and CEOs know that you are coming."

I decided to ask him about his comment at the beginning of the conversation.

"What did I say the other day that made you think you do Enterprise Architecture?"

Nothing happened for a short time, then he blasted me. "I don't THINK I do enterprise architecture! I actually DO it. You're the one who THINKS he does it. Tell me, Simon, how many enterprises have you ACTUALLY DESIGNED? And I mean ENTERPRISES, not the technologies they use or the processes they're involved in? And if you have designed any Enterprises, how many of those designs have you BROUGHT TO FRUITION and BEEN ACCOUNTABLE FOR WHETHER THEY WORKED OR NOT? I'm not even sure you know what ENTERPRISE is."

I sat there, fuming, but not knowing what to say.

He continued, "What do you say to that?"

Angry, I said, "Enterprise is what brought me all the way over to America, to work for you. I took a calculated risk because I thought it would be valuable. Please don't tell me that I don't know what enterprise is."

"Good," he replied, not shouting any more, "So now you know what enterprise architecture is. Creating the structures and spaces for our people to take calculated risks because they think the result will be valuable."

I sat there, stunned by this revelation.

"Look," he continued more calmly, "What you said changed the way that I saw things. You did the same in Tokyo for the President and me. That's very valuable, because it's people like he and I who can actually redesign the enterprise's architecture. We executives can drive people to do things differently. We invest in changes that reshape or restructure the company, and make sure it delivers greater performance. You have a role called Enterprise Architecture, but we executives are accountable for the design, delivery and performance of the enterprise. So we also do 'enterprise architecture', and we need people like you to join in, provide leadership, influence us with new ideas, and for the ones we choose to invest in, to share our commitment to making them succeed. I think you can be fantastic if you want to be, but the first thing I need you to do is to express yourself as part of our enterprise's leadership community, not think that you design the company. You didn't answer my question. How many enterprises have you designed, and been accountable for whether those designs actually work or not?"

"None."

"Right, because that's not your job. OK?"

"I thought that it was."

"Do you still think that it is?"

"I'd like it to be."

"So you want my job?"

"No, I don't think I could do your job."

"Who knows? Maybe you could one day."

"Thank you."

Michael then turned the conversation in an intriguing direction. He asked me what my metaphor was for designing an enterprise's architecture. My reply was that the closest one was a building, because that was the origin of architecture.

"I can see the value in that," he replied, "Whenever someone says the word architecture, buildings are the first things that come to my mind. But I'd like you to consider something which I find very obvious but does not fit that metaphor."

I said nothing, so he carried on.

"Buildings are not enterprises. While they certainly have architecture, they have no enterprise."

Seeing that I still had nothing to say, he carried on.

"On the other hand, by definition, enterprises have enterprise *and* architecture. It's true that there are quite a few design concepts from buildings architecture that we can apply to an enterprise – how they integrate aesthetically and functionally with the surrounding environment, the purposes they are designed for, their shape and structure, the spaces they contain for people to exploit in enterprising and enjoyable ways, and so on. There's something else, too. If you look at two or more buildings with a similar purpose that were designed by the same architect – office blocks, or airport terminals, or houses – often, no two will be the same; same kind of building, same purpose, same architect, probably many of the same technologies, but different architectures. Why do you think that is?"

That caught me off guard. I was expecting to just sit and listen to his speech and think about whether I agreed with what he was saying, but he had finished it with a question.

"I don't know of any two buildings with the same purpose that have been designed by the same architect, so I am not sure how to answer your question."

"OK, how about these. You're from England, right. Which airport did you leave to come here?"

"London Heathrow."

"Well, who designed Terminal Five at Heathrow Airport?"

"I'm sorry I don't know."

"Richard Rogers, or Lord Rogers, if you prefer. He also designed Terminal Four at Madrid Barajas Airport in Spain. Believe me when I say that their architectures are not the same. I have been to both of them and experienced the differences. Why do you think that is?"

"For a start, they are in very different environments. And I don't suppose the people in Spain wanted the same airport terminal as the people in England."

"No, I don't suppose they did. And do you think the architect himself wanted to design the same airport terminal twice."

I was starting to see Michael's point. Together, the owner of the building and the architect would want to create something unique each time. I asked him whether this was what he meant.

"Yes, it is. A vital part of architecture is, as I see it, self-expression. That's also a vital element in someone's enterprise."

"I can see that's true, but I'd also like to challenge it."

"Good."

"What if the owner of a building wants to recreate the same architecture many times over, in different parts of the world?"

"Give me an example."

"A hotel group, or a restaurant chain, for example."

"You mean like a hotel group like Hyatt? How many of their hotels have you been to?"

Without needing to answer his question, I could see where my challenge had taken us. While there must be some standard design themes, I had to assume that each of the hotels in a group is also different in some way. Without being to a few more of them to find out, I had no first-hand experience of how different they might be.

"Just the one, with you. But I can see where you're taking this."

"Good. If I took you to the 87$^{th}$ floor bar at the Grand Hyatt in Shanghai's Pudong district, I can tell you it would be in a different building, and a different experience, from the New York Bar in Tokyo."

"But there must be some similarities in terms of the Brand values and Service."

"Absolutely. And that's where I start with my enterprise architecture. How people experience our Brands and Service, wherever we appear in the world and their lives. Day in, day out, we need to put on performances out there that make our audiences go 'Wow!'"

"Performances? Audiences? You mean like in the theatre or a movie?"

"Those are some other interesting metaphors. I like the movie one better for a reason I'll tell you in a moment. But our business is interactive. You can react to a movie, but you can't interact with it. However, we can certainly learn from movie-makers about creating a cohesive experience for our audiences with an enterprise that exists in many locations at once. The

President in Japan was right. Redesigning where things happen in an enterprise can sometimes lead to a lack of cohesion that, in time, damages the very experiences and performances it was meant to improve, thereby impacting the integrity of our Brand and Service."

I asked him what movies could show us about that.

"Well, here's a good example. Not that far from here, in TriBeCa, you'll find the 8 Hook and Ladder fire station. Go and have a look, if you get the chance. That's the Ghostbusters fire station. Well, one of them. They used it for the external shots, but the internals were filmed at another fire station a whole continent away, over in Los Angeles. They did the same with the Library sequences. Movie-makers do that all the time. I'll bet you didn't notice."

I said that, no, I hadn't noticed.

"Well, that's the sort of cohesion we need to make sure we achieve with our performance as an enterprise. Our audiences should enjoy a great experience without ever knowing or caring about the internal structure of our business, or where any parts of it are located. That's why I liked your idea of virtual hubs. I want to use that to get the company to think differently about how we design ourselves and where we locate things, but most of all to make how we appear in our customer's life experiences into the true hub of our enterprise's architecture."

"Is that the same as a customer-centric architecture?"

"No. It's an experiences-centric architecture."

"Oh."

He concluded, "That's it, we've run out of time for this discussion. I think you know what I need you to do for me. Make sure you call me before you start work with each business, so I can tell you where they fit in our Corporate Strategy. Stay in some nice hotels, find some interesting bars. Let me know if you need anything."

And then, just as I stood up to leave, he hit me with a punch line. "By the way, the biggest difference between buildings and enterprises is that buildings can't change their own architecture. Have a great trip."

I walked out of his office and straight past Trudy. I went downstairs and found Lucy.

"Michael just blasted me."

"I told you the other day that he would. What did you say to him?"

"It doesn't matter. But he just fundamentally redefined what I thought enterprise architecture was all about. And I should have known all along, if only I'd stopped to think what the word 'enterprise' actually means."

"Sounds like you need a break. Go out for a walk."

"Thanks."

I walked outside and decided to make the phone call that I had thought about on the plane back from Tokyo, to my former CIO in London. It was just after 2:30 P.M. in New York, which made it 7:30 P.M. back home.

"Hello, this is Ian Taylor."

"Ian, this is Simon. Simon Rathbone."

"Hello, Simon."

"I need to talk to you. Do you have a moment?"

"Sure. Where are you?"

"New York. This is the new job I told you about. How are you doing?"

"Just fine, Simon, just fine. Are you still angry with me?"

There was no distinctive tone in his voice, for me to judge how he was reacting.

"No, I'm not still angry with you, and I think I need your advice."

"What do you want to ask me?"

In truth, I wasn't sure, but it was good to speak to Ian again. I also didn't know whether to apologize or not for my behavior before I finished working for him. No apologies, no regrets...

"I started over here a couple of weeks ago, reporting to the global CTO. When I told the CEO that I'm an Enterprise Architect he seemed to confuse my role with his. He's already changed things so that I work directly for him and took me to Tokyo to meet the President there and talk about something he called structural performance. What he regards as enterprise architecture is nothing like what we always thought it was. Now he's sending me around the world to visit some more of the company's businesses and design a repeatable journey for making EA an integral part of how the company is managed."

"Well done. Sounds like you're getting on really well. But what can I do to help?"

"You know me as well as anyone, professionally. Will I be able to do it?"

"Yes, I think you will."

That was what I needed to hear.

"Thank you."

"You're welcome."

There was a pause, so I asked Ian, "How are you doing?"

"Very well, thank you Simon. Look, as far as you can without breaching confidentiality, let me know how you get along. I'm really interested in what you're going to do, and how it fits with the things I'm working on now."

"I will. Can I ask you something else?"

"Sure, go ahead."

"Do you still agree with what our CEO did with EA and IT?"

"Not all of it, no. Most of it, yes. But as I still work for her that's all I'm prepared to say."

"Did you think it was wrong for her to give EA to Corporate Strategy?"

"Still the same old Simon. Look, that's the past already. You've got a great new challenge. It doesn't matter whether what happened before was right or wrong. Let it go."

I wanted to tell him that I wasn't still the same old Simon and to ask him why he thought that I was. Also, the answer to the question I had asked him might help with what I now had to achieve. However, instead of trying again, I decided to leave things there and end the call.

"I've got to go now Ian. Thanks for the advice."

"Goodbye, Simon. You're welcome."

Our conversation finished there. I appreciated his kindness, although stung by his 'same old Simon' remark. The distance between us was still very tangible, and I had a journey to embark upon.

---

## Observations

- The level of dynamism in an enterprise is a core consideration in designing its architecture.

- Great Enterprise Architects influence how business leaders think and act.

- Enterprise and architecture have meanings that existed long before they were combined into Enterprise Architecture. To truly engage business leaders, EA must reflect those original meanings.

- Business executives are, in practice, the architects of their enterprise.

- Buildings are the most common metaphor for articulating EA concepts. Other, less obvious, metaphors - such as movies - can help demonstrate the differences between the architectures of buildings and enterprises.

- Choosing the focal point, or 'hub', of your enterprise's architecture is a fundamental design decision.

---

# THE JOURNEY

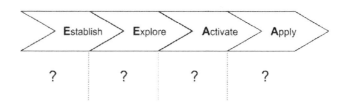

"Double-E, Double-A"

# EIGHT
## Sydney, Australia

In Sydney, I learned the first of two apparently paradoxical lessons about architecture. If you get too close to the details, or the technologies, it's impossible to see the architecture at all. But the apparent paradox - which I will come back to later - is that successful architecture is very much about the details.

As this was the first stop on my journey to create a repeatable process for EA as a strategic capability, I wasn't sure whether to start at the end ("Apply") and work backwards, or the beginning ("Establish") and work forwards. How would someone be sure, without knowing how they would apply something in practice, what to establish in the first place? But I also wanted to avoid being constrained at the outset by knowing too much about how it would finally work.

Another lesson I first learned in Sydney, from exploring the history of the Opera House, was that innovations in architecture can mean figuring out some of the practicalities later. I found many more examples, like the Petronas Towers in Kuala Lumpur. In the case of the Opera House, this was much, much later. If you're not familiar with the story of the building, its design, the client, the architect and the engineers, I recommend you look it up. Suffice it to say that, at the opening ceremony, in 1973, after an investment process that had taken a quarter of a century from the original idea - including sixteen years from the time the winning design was chosen - the architect was not invited and got no mention at all.

So I opted to start with Establish rather than Apply, and see where that took me:

Michael had told me about our Australian business before I left New York. He had focused on different structural ratios from the ones he'd used for Japan. "The potential contribution of Enterprise Architecture is likely to be different every time," he explained. This time, they included Operating Income per Dollar of Staff Expenses, and Staff Expenses as a percentage of Total Operating Expenses. The first of these ratios indicated that, while Australia was achieving steady year-on-year growth in revenues and profits, there seemed to be a deeper, downward trend in the productivity of their investment in people. Yet, according to the second ratio, Staff Expenses were slowly increasing as a proportion of Total Operating Expenses. "People are our enterprise," Michael had told me. "We need to invest our people money wisely."

He had also told me, in utter confidence, that the longer-term plans for Australia were probably to sell the business. So by thinking and acting as investors ourselves, we could best encourage that business to develop in a way that would be most valuable to a potential buyer – or to us, if we chose to keep it. "Keep those two scenarios in mind in everything you do. But never indicate to anyone what we are thinking, not even with a flicker of your eye."

On the first day of working with our Australian colleagues, I had a meeting scheduled at 9:30 A.M. with the local CEO, Matt. However, when I arrived, there were two people in the room.

"How's it going?" asked the CEO, "I'm Matt, and this is Craig, my CIO. I reckoned you'd want him to be here, as I expect you'll want to talk about IT."

I was beginning to get very frustrated with how much people associated EA with IT. It was getting in the way of the conversations I now needed to have. However, sitting there with the Australian CEO was not the time to get into a discussion, which he would probably find abstract, about the true meaning of EA. My decision was to simply conduct the meeting without mentioning IT at all, and see how that went.

"Thank you, Matt. It's good to meet you, Craig. First, let me explain why I'm here. We're working on a repeatable process - a journey - for making Enterprise Architecture a core capability in the way we manage our businesses. That journey has four stages, and Michael has asked me to work with some of our key businesses around the world to map it out and start applying it in practice."

I placed in front of them my one-page picture of the Double-E Double-A journey with the first stage highlighted.

"I'd like your help to describe how we first 'Establish' the role of EA in our business management before we then 'Explore' in more depth how best to go about it, and so on."

Craig, the CIO, asked the first question. "Won't it be the same every time? Why do you need us to help you, rather than just design the process back home in the USA and then simply tell us what it is?"

I almost reacted to this challenge by arguing with it, but stopped myself. It was an old habit that would undoubtedly die hard. Instead, I answered, "That may well be true. That's one reason I'm here - to find out, with your help. On the other hand, although on paper there might be one journey, I'd like to allow for the possibility that it might, in reality, be different every time depending on where Enterprise Architecture can make the best contribution, and on what we encounter along the way. Would that be OK?"

"Sure," Craig replied.

"Thank you."

Next, Matt spoke. "I'm happy, now, with what you're asking us to help you with. Let's get you and Craig working on this together. Show me what you both come up with before you go back to America."

"I'm actually going to Hong Kong next, but I'll certainly update you before I leave. Can I ask you a question about your business results?"

"Ok, ask."

"I was looking, in particular, at the productivity ratio of Operating Income to Staff Expenses, and I'd like to explore with you what we can do to reverse its decline."

Matt said nothing, immediately. Instead he looked over the spectacles he was wearing, and past my shoulder, with no expression on his face. Then he turned his eyes to look at me. "Show me your numbers," he said, tightly.

I reached down for my backpack, watched by Matt and Craig, and took out my laptop. "They're on here," I said, as I opened the cover.

Sometimes computers can take an age to come on, even from hibernate. When it did, I opened Excel and showed them the spreadsheet and graphs from their business results. "I got these from your annual accounts, as any investor could," I said, as they peered intensely at my screen.

Matt said, drily, "Count yourself lucky you don't work for me. I need to take my next meeting. Come and see me again before you leave for China."

Craig and I stood up and left Matt's office. "Come with me," he said. So I followed him as he turned through a nearby door and climbed up some stairs. We emerged through another door onto the roof. "I'd jump now, if I were you. Just what kind of strategy was that?"

"What kind of strategy was what?"

He told me that the figures I had shown Matt were not ones that they monitored. I had surprised him with bad news about the business he ran. No warning, just straight in there. The chances of Matt being supportive now were close to zero.

There was a part of me that accepted what Craig was saying and agreed that I had gotten it wrong. But, having spent time with Michael on the Tokyo trip, and remembering that I was to think and act as an investor, there was now another side to this conversation.

"Well, I'm more than a little concerned that I was the one that had to place these numbers in front of you both. Frankly, I would expect you to be monitoring ratios like this, and using them to guide decisions about how to improve your business's performance, by investing in changing your enterprise's architecture. I'm sure the last thing you would want is for us, your investor, to know more about your performance than you do."

"No Enterprise Architect has talked to me like this before. I'll ask you again – what kind of strategy are you following here?"

"One in which we work together to enhance the structural performance of your business, which means first sharing our observations on what aspects of that performance would most benefit from innovation, redesign and investment."

"And you want to convince Matt that reshaping our IT Architecture will improve the ratio of Operating Income to Staff Expenses."

"No. Redesigning the structure of your enterprise, not simply the IT it uses. For all we know, it may need no IT changes at all. We're clearly talking about a very different scope for EA."

"You can say that again. Go on."

As the sun set over the Harbour Bridge, I told Craig about my journey, so far - how I had crossed over from thinking EA was centered on IT to making it centered on the structure and space we give people for their enterprise to flourish; that we need to establish how an enterprise is performing structurally, before knowing what investments to make in changing, or preserving, that performance. Craig asked me many questions, which I thought were rooted in an unspoken concern that I had provoked in him, about the IT-centric nature of his own role as CIO.

It was almost night when he said, "Enough for one day. I've got a meeting with Matt tomorrow. Can I explain this to him? As his CIO, I think that's for me to do."

I said that was fine, that I wanted to think about the Establish stage of my EEAA journey, and perhaps we could get together again after he had seen the CEO.

"Take a look at that," Craig said as he turned towards the harbor, "Circular Quay. Isn't it magic?"

And magic it was, with the green-and-cream ferries ploughing backwards and forwards, the Bridge and the Opera House lit up on either side of us, and the trains pulling in and out of the harbor station.

"I read somewhere that they fired the architect who designed the Opera House, or he resigned, depending on whose story you believe," he said, looking at me rather intently. "Let's go have a drink and some dinner."

We walked uphill in the direction of the Bridge and into the oldest area of Sydney, The Rocks. We had a German beer in a Bavarian pub a very long way from Bavaria. Then we went to dinner at a Thai restaurant, not quite so far from Thailand, which was designed like a refectory, with one long, shared table. "Thanks for an interesting day, my friend," Craig said after dinner, as he left for home and I headed back to my hotel in the harbor.

I went straight to bed, but stayed awake for an hour, or so, thinking about the Establish stage of my journey and what it might comprise.

The following day, I borrowed a desk in Craig's department to work some more on my thoughts. I sat among his IT Architects, feeling like a foreigner. Which, of course, I was, literally. But what I mean is that I didn't feel at home any more with people who were doing the very thing that, until recently, I had also been doing.

Here's what I concluded the Establish stage should focus on:

<u>Strategy</u> – What EA as a formal discipline, is, overall, promising to achieve; the key principles it needs to apply; and its core tactics for achieving success.[2]

---

[2] Author's note:

Simon is using the form of strategy that he witnessed in FruITion, although he dismissed it as 'wrong' at the time!

<u>Scope</u> - The boundaries and main elements of an enterprise's architecture and how they inter-relate.

<u>Guiding Ratios</u> - The structural performance ratios that guide the enterprise's investments in changing or preserving its architecture.

<u>Key Measure</u> - The ultimate motive that EA represents.

I added these headings to my picture of the EEAA journey:

These seemed to be the four main things that we would always need to establish before progressing any further. As I was sitting there trying to decide whether there should be any more, one of the IT Architects said to me, "Are you Simon?" When I said that I was, he said that Craig was on the phone from the CEO's office, asking for me to go up and join them in their meeting.

There was only one way to walk into Matt's office, and that was assertively, even though I was not sure what line he would take after the previous day's meeting.

"Sit down, Simon," he said.

I replied "Sure," and sat down.

"Now, I can't tell you how I angry I was with you after our meeting yesterday." I said nothing, just looked at him, so he continued, "I even phoned Michael to tell him. Guess what he replied."

"I'm sorry, I have no idea."

It seems that Michael told Matt that I was a genius, and that he was to take notice of everything I said.

Matt continued, "So have you got any more surprises for me about my own business?"

"No, I don't think so, but there is something I'd like your observations on."

Matt asked me what that was, so I showed him my EEAA journey again, and what I had so far decided about the first stage. He looked at it, paused for a moment, and then asked me the answer to the final question it posed: what is the ultimate motive, and measure of success, for Enterprise Architecture? I was going to answer, but he asked another question: was that supposed to be a measure of Enterprise Architecture as something that people did, or of the architecture of an enterprise, or of the people whose title is Enterprise Architect? That led me to think about the differences between these three things and how they influenced each other. I also realized that Matt had effectively raised the question that I had avoided in our previous meeting, about the true meaning of EA, although interestingly, in terms of its ultimate motive rather than its scope.

"I'll have a shot at an answer," I said, "and let's see what happens. I think it should be the ultimate measure of the architecture of an enterprise. To me, the other two are contributing factors."

Craig intervened, "I'm getting uncomfortable with where this looks to be going."

"That worries me," said Matt, "Why?"

"I can't see how my Enterprise Architects can be responsible for the performance of the entire enterprise."

Matt answered him very quickly indeed, without apparently taking any time to think. "They're not. I am."

Craig was silent, and so was I. Between Michael, first, and now Matt, a common thread was developing. In both of their cases, the Chief Executive Officer, once faced with the idea of Enterprise Architecture being about (not surprisingly) the architecture of the enterprise, concluded that they were the ultimate designer and decision-maker. In my mind, that made the CEO into the Chief Enterprise Architect, the "CEA". It would then follow, I thought, that we who carry the Enterprise Architect title must be their 'assistant architects', and maybe others are, too.

Matt continued, still talking to Craig, "I think your Enterprise Architects need to be working for me."

Craig quite obviously did not like this at all. "With all due respect, Matt, I think that would be wrong. Many of them are technical specialists in IT Architecture."

"I didn't mean your IT Architects. I specifically meant your Enterprise Architects. Is that right Simon? I don't mean they need to report to me, they can still report to you if that makes sense, but they need to be working for me. Come on, this is Australia. Let's not get hung up on who reports to whom."

He turned to me, which I took to mean he was looking for an answer to the question he asked me in the middle of all that.

"Yes, Matt. Whoever the Enterprise Architects report to in the structure, they need to be working for the Chief Executive – on the CEO's design for the enterprise, how it's being delivered, and how well it's performing."

"Thought so," said Matt, "Still got worries Craig? If so, speak out."

"No," said Craig, "No worries."

Matt turned back to the ultimate measure of success. He asked me why it would be valuable to have one. I answered that it was rooted in certain aspects of systems theory, where each 'agent' in a system has an overall measure of success – a 'fitness criterion', in the jargon - that determines their interactions with other 'agents'. Here we were talking about the people that represented Enterprise Architecture being agents within the enterprise system. That was why they needed to know EA's ultimate measure of success.

Matt thanked me for the explanation, although I wasn't sure how much he was interested in hearing about systems theory. He said that he preferred to look at the question from the perspective of being an outside observer, standing back and seeing the enterprise from some distance away, rather than being either up close to the enterprise or on the inside looking out. If you start too close, he said, you lose a sense of what the architecture is, and how it contributes to the wider environment. "For example, try standing up close to the Opera House. All you'll see is ceramic tiles. Once you've stood far enough away to appreciate its shape and surroundings, you can always get up close later, now you have the context. And then, when you get inside the structure, there will be even more to admire. But now imagine trying to see the architecture of the Opera House only from the inside-out, and never from the outside-in. Concrete arches, wood, things like that. Through the windows, you'd see ceramic-tiled, curved roofs, and whatever is beyond them. What would you make of that?"

I thought both Craig and I could see Matt's point. I asked if that meant he knew what we should therefore make the overall EA measure of success, to which he replied, "The enterprise's contribution to the communities, or markets, in which it plays a part. I appreciate that's a bit too vague. More specifically, keeping its commitments to its stakeholders – in particular, the promises that our Brands represent, that we mean to be inherent in our Service, and in our Products and Services; also the promises that we have effectively made to our shareholders, regulators and so on."

He continued, "Constantly keeping those commitments takes a combination of existing business operations and investments in change. So I think the ultimate measure of EA success, which I realize is not a metric, is how well we combine business operations and new investments in a shape and structure that keeps our commitments to our stakeholders."

"Now we've found the Key Measure, let's go backwards up your other three topics. We've got some examples of the Guiding Ratios that you confronted me with, yesterday…"

I interrupted him, "They are real examples of where the EEAA journey is different every time. Michael and I were in Tokyo, just recently, and found different Guiding Ratios to articulate where EA can make the best contribution."

"That's a great example. Thank you for pointing it out," said Matt. "Let's have a short break, then tackle the next subject on your list."

After our short break, Matt continued, "So let's move onto Scope. For me, the scope of our enterprise's architecture certainly includes how it appears to the outside world, and the impacts that we have on people's lives and experiences, out there. Then, if we step inside our enterprise, it must include the organization we've designed to achieve those impacts and to keep our other commitments. In my mind, our organization equals the structure in which we place our own people, plus the relationships that we have with partners and suppliers."

Craig asked, "Sorry, Matt, I got a bit confused there. Are you saying that we should regard our partners and suppliers as part of our organization?"

Matt replied, "Only to the extent to which they are fulfilling what we need from them. Not when they are working for someone else."

"OK," said Craig, "I get that."

I said that I had remembered something that Michael had told me on the way to Tokyo.

"What did he say?" asked Matt.

"That the customer has the process, and that we have to figure out how best to appear in it. I remember telling him this was the opposite of how I had previously seen things, with customers appearing in our processes."

Craig commented, "That's pretty revolutionary. But it makes sense."

Matt continued, "Let's widen that a bit, without losing sight of Michael's principle, and say that the market has the processes in which we, as a business, can decide to appear."

"And most of the knowledge, too," Craig pointed out, "And the technologies."

I told Matt and Craig that I saw a picture in what we were saying and asked if I could draw it on Matt's whiteboard. "No worries," said Matt, so I stood up, picked up a marker - remembering to check if it was for whiteboards or flipcharts - and drew this diagram:

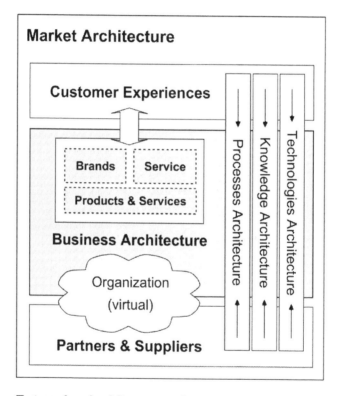

**Enterprise Architecture - Scope (Theme?)**

"What strikes me," I observed, "Is how much – or should I say how little - of this scope formalized EA has been focusing on and actively influencing, so far. Also, that it's tended to approach the entire architecture from our internal technologies-outwards, rather than market-inwards. I was just wondering what would happen if we designed buildings that way. This represents a very different school of enterprise architecture."

Matt and Craig said that they really liked the picture, and Matt asked if he could leave it on the whiteboard to show some of the other executives. I told him it was good of him to ask, and that I would be absolutely delighted if that meant he could put it to valuable use. I also copied it down so I could formalize it later, alongside my EEAA journey. If it turned out to be a useful model, I would also have to think of a name for it, to encapsulate its theme.

"So," said Matt, "We've done the Measure, the Guiding Ratios and the Scope. Now, finally, what about the first item on your list, Strategy?"

Craig suggested that we make the strategy about the formal discipline of Enterprise Architecture, rather than the enterprise's architecture itself. I could see that he was fishing to take leadership of that strategy.

Matt probably saw that too, because he asked Craig, and not me, what the Promise of that strategy should be.

Craig reminded us of what we had said about the Measure, which was about how well the enterprise kept its commitments to stakeholders with a blend of existing operations and new investments. He said he saw Enterprise Architecture as primarily about influencing investments in change, rather than day-to-day operations. Matt replied that he broadly agreed, but that there must be a role for Enterprise Architecture to directly or indirectly influence people involved in our business operations - which could include the company's customers - to best exploit the architecture that the company had already invested in. "So," he asked Craig, "With that in mind, what do you see as the strategy's Promise?"

"My first thought," replied Craig, "Is that it needs to express a continuum. What I mean is that a strategy for EA doesn't ever finish. It's not about promising an eventual outcome, like finishing a building, but an ongoing return on our investment in doing it."

I found myself agreeing with him. "I think that's right. I used to think that strategies for EA were about achieving a 'to be' architecture, typically via something called a roadmap." Craig smiled knowingly, as I said this. "But, following a conversation with some of our colleagues in Canada, I realized that the chances of EA delivering on that promise are very low indeed, which means it is a promise EA should never make, to itself or anyone else. Most of a 'to be' architecture often seems to stay on the drawing-board. The enterprise usually picks-and-chooses which parts of it to invest in, and not all of those investments will actually work out as planned. I'm increasingly sure that some kind of continuum is a more sane and realistic promise for EA to make and keep." Just after I said this, I wasn't sure whether I should have said 'sane', but neither Matt nor Craig seemed to take offense.

Matt picked up on the theme. He said he was just thinking out loud about the value of what we were calling 'to be' architectures. The first thought that emerged was that there needed to be more than one, given that strategists like him need to be working with multiple scenarios. There was not much value in a roadmap if it showed only one road! Matt's second thought was that the contribution of any 'to be' scenarios was not that the enterprise would actually promise to achieve any of them, but that they would be used to decide on how best to invest in changing the enterprise's shape or structure. "With the Guiding Ratios as a reflection of current structural performance, then the primary contribution of a strategy for EA would be to ensure we innovate in our investment plans to produce a higher-performing structure than we would otherwise have done. Put more simply, by combining both formal and informal 'enterprise architecture', we produce better results than the latter on its own."

Craig suddenly bounded out of his chair and said, "I've got it!" He took a marker, drew a box on Matt's whiteboard and inside it wrote:

*Enhancing Enterprise Performance*
*With Structural Innovations*

Matt and I both looked at Craig as if he had just produced a rabbit out of a hat. I think we even broke into spontaneous applause.

"Magic! That's it!" Matt declared.

"Thanks," replied Craig, slightly out of breath.

"I like it," I said, immediately wishing I had said something more enthusiastic. "Fantastic!"

Matt announced it was time for another break, then we would do the rest of the strategy. In the corridor outside his office, when it was just the two of us, he told me that I needed to be more relaxed about letting other people be the architects.

"Your role is to provoke, lead and facilitate. Craig and I, and our executive colleagues, are the architects of the business here in Australia. If you're acting as one of our investors, then there's a point at which you'll have a conflict of interest if you try to join in too much, or have too much control. You're giving us leadership in becoming better enterprise architects. When you stick to that role, you're very valuable. Remember that we're all in this together."

After the short break, the three of us collaborated in defining the Key Principles and Core Tactics to go with our Promise. Here's what we decided upon:

### Promise
Enhancing Enterprise Performance
With Structural Innovations

### Key Principles

- The structural performance of an enterprise depends on its architecture.
- An enterprise has architecture, whether formalized or not.
- The actual shape and structure of an enterprise's architecture is the aggregated output of all its investments in change.
- The value of a structural innovation depends on the wider architectural context.
- Enterprise Architecture is about scenarios, not certainties.

### Core Tactics

- Bring together formal and informal Enterprise Architecture.
- Use structural performance ratios to make, monitor and exploit architectural choices and investments.
- Cohesively apply architectural themes across investments in change.

- Evaluate and select innovations in the context of the enterprise's actual architecture.

- Use multiple scenarios, not roadmaps, to make architectural decisions.

We agreed that this was only a first draft strategy, and a generic one at that. It was not about any enterprise in particular. But it was unlike any strategy for EA that any of us had seen before.

Matt and Craig told me that they wanted to work together on an Australian derivative of this generic strategy. Would I leave that to them, if they kept me informed of what they decided? Conscious of Matt's advice, and bearing in mind I was soon due to leave for Hong Kong, I told them I thought that would be ideal. Likewise, I asked them if I could use our generic strategy as I traveled on around the world, working with other businesses in the group. They were very happy for me to do so.

Finally, I asked them a question that had been lurking in my mind as we were working on the Strategy. In it, we had mentioned both 'shape' and 'structure'. So far in my journey, I had only been thinking about structure. What was the difference?

Craig took me to the window of Matt's office. "Look at the Opera House. Then, if you're still wondering, ask us again."

I looked at that stunning work of architecture and answered my own question. The shape of an enterprise is the boundaries of its structure within the wider world. Those boundaries, and the messages they represent, would be more or less cohesive, depending on the design (or lack of it). From the outside world's perspective, shape was likely to be a much more important consideration than internal structure.

Matt's final words in that paradigm-shifting discussion were, "The architect designed the shape that you see, Simon. Much, much later the engineers designed the internal structure to support it. I think we should consider that happened the right way around, don't you? Oh, and by the way, one of the reasons, as I understand it, that the architect lost the support of his client was that he wanted too much control. Thank you for your inspiration, Simon, and enjoy the journey ahead."

## Observations

- Great architecture can sometimes mean figuring out the practicalities after the design has been chosen.

- Political considerations are essential in Enterprise Architecture.

- An architect has a responsibility to guide and oversee - but not necessarily control - the realization of the design.

- The ultimate measure of EA success is how well the enterprise meets it commitments to its stakeholders.

- Markets have processes, knowledge and technologies. Enterprises participate in, and can add to, the architecture of a market.

- A strategy for EA is founded on a continuum, not a destination.

# NINE

## Hong Kong, China

I arrived in Hong Kong from Australia on a hot, humid Friday evening. Trudy, Michael's PA, had booked me a luxurious hotel room on Hong Kong Island. As I stepped outside to explore my surroundings, slightly unsteady from the heat and humidity, it struck me that from the skyscrapers to the street vendors, enterprise was crammed in, vibrantly, everywhere.

And yet, as I discovered the next day, it is still possible to step back from all that enterprise and observe it from a peaceful distance by taking the tram to the top of the Peak, which is the highest point on the

**119**

Island. There, first thing on Saturday morning, I found myself in calm, wooded surroundings with people out running, walking, doing Tai Chi, or simply sitting quietly. There were low-level clouds hanging over the city below, so all I could see of it were the unmoving tops of the taller buildings. I could hear the city, and its enterprising people, more than I could see it, but those sounds seem to emphasize the Peak's peace, rather than disrupt it.

When I arrived at our offices on Queens Road on Monday, I found that the local President was away on business. They told me that the Commercial Director, Mrs. Zhang, would be looking after me, and showed me to a desk in her department. My initial meeting with Mrs. Zhang was scheduled for Tuesday morning, so I had an entire day to myself. I used the opportunity to establish some Guiding Ratios for our Hong Kong business. However, whichever ones I chose, I found I had a problem - they all showed stable or improving performance.

Before leaving Sydney, I had called Michael to get the background on our Hong Kong operation. He told me that we were in something of a 'holding pattern', monitoring carefully how the longer-term political climate might impact our interests there. By all means, I should help them tune their operating performance, if there seemed to be low-risk innovations that could do so, but otherwise simply collaborate with them on assembling the EEAA journey.

Based on the evidence of the Guiding Ratios, and bearing in mind Michael's instructions, it looked like there was nothing to do architecturally except make sure that any changes our Hong Kong colleagues invested in both protected and sustained their performance, rather than disrupted it.

Returning to the Double-E Double-A journey, having assembled the Establish stage with Australia, the next one to define was Explore. I imagined for a moment that I was the architect of a city rather than a company. What would I want to explore, before I actively started on any new design? These are the four things I chose: Stakeholders, Culture and Politics, Constraints, and Architectural Themes. I added them to my emerging process, like this:

The next day, when I met Mrs. Zhang, I talked her through the objectives of the work I was doing, showed her the unfinished EEAA journey, and the results of my time with Matt and Craig in Australia. My host was very interested, unerringly polite and supportive. "I will introduce you to our IT people," she said, "They have an Enterprise Architecture team." I thanked her, and went on to show her the Guiding Ratios that I had worked on the day before. She smiled, walked gracefully over to a cabinet, took out a file and opened it for me to read. There, in front of me, were many of the same ratios, and some more besides!

I then told her that I was concerned she might be regarding Enterprise Architecture as centered on IT, as she was sending me to work with the IT department. She replied, "It's OK, I don't, and I can see from the approach you are taking that you don't, either. But the Enterprise Architects do. They seem to feel that their friends in IT are more important stakeholders in what they do than my executive colleagues and I. For example, when I show them these business ratios, nothing happens. Instead, they talk to us about trends in the IT market, show us diagrams that are mainly about the things that IT people are interested in, and tell us how they are working closely with our IT employees and suppliers. I thought that you could help them become more enterprise-centric, while they help you design the next stage of your EEAA journey. That would be very valuable to me."

I replied, "In that case, I will be delighted to do so."

"Very good. I will introduce you to their leader, who is English like you. His name is Mr. Paul, Alan Paul, although he prefers that we call him Al."

She told her secretary to ask Mr. Paul to join us, which he did within five minutes. Mrs. Zhang told Al that I was there to help them with their Enterprise Architecture. With the President, she was certain that the company's investment in EA was one that would grow in value over the years. She told him that I was working with a number of EA teams in our businesses around the world to better integrate formal Enterprise Architecture with mainstream strategy and management. This was a special opportunity for Al and his team to contribute to, and learn from, that work.

Mrs. Zhang then suggested that Al and I continue the discussions on our own, stood up, and showed us to the door of her office. As we left, she silently handed me her folder containing her ratios.

Al and I took the elevator down two floors and went to his desk. I have to admit that I didn't really like him much, based on first impressions, but tried to make sure that those feelings did not overly affect our work.

Al asked, "How do you want to play this? Shall we start with our Blueprints?"

I showed him the folder that Mrs. Zhang had given me. "Have you seen this before?"

He opened the folder and flicked through the pages inside. "No, I can't say that I have."

"Mrs. Zhang just lent it to me. It's become my practice to explore the structural performance ratios of a business before deciding where the work that you and I do can best make a contribution, and who we'll most need to influence to be successful. They're called EA Guiding Ratios. First, not all businesses are monitoring these kinds of ratios, and second, yours make especially interesting reading."

Al was looking puzzled. "Why?"

"Because they indicate that, at the moment, the best strategy for EA here is to protect the architecture you already have. The Guiding Ratios are all looking good."

"To be honest, I'm not really getting what you're telling me. What difference can my team and I make to these kinds of numbers?"

"You influence people that make investment decisions, right?"

"No, not really."

"Oh. Who do you influence?"

"Project teams, mainly."

"Business change projects?"

"IT projects."

"So you're overseeing the IT architecture rather than the enterprise's architecture?"

Al was looking more uncomfortable as the conversation progressed.

"No, my friend, we're doing Enterprise Architecture. If you'd let me show you our Blueprints, maybe that would help you."

I let him show me their Blueprints, which were in another folder. What I found especially striking was that in all their diagrams, IT was portrayed as bigger, and with more detail, than the wider business. Also, our business's customers were not shown at all, let alone the experiences they have in which we appear.

Rather than say any of this to Al, as I didn't think it would help at this stage, I placed the two folders – Guiding Ratios and Blueprints – on his desk, leaving a gap about the size of another folder between them. "So, if we have on the one hand the enterprise's EA Guiding Ratios and on the other your architectural Blueprints, what joins them together? Putting it another way, what value do Mrs. Zhang and her executive colleagues see in your Blueprints?"

Still looking rattled by the conversation, Al asked, "Why should I care?"

"First, because your business's executives are the key stakeholders in EA. Second, because they believe that you and your team can make a much bigger contribution to the success of this business than you currently do. That's why Mrs. Zhang has asked me to work with you." I realized I was taking a political gamble by acting as a messenger between Mrs. Zhang and Al, but I reckoned I could get them working better together by the time I left for Paris.

"Well," said Al, "I'm sorry, but I'm not convinced. But here's what I want you to do. Let's have a workshop with me and my team, and you can be our facilitator. Set whatever agenda you like, and see where it gets us. I wish you luck. We can't even get everyone to agree on a single definition for Enterprise Architecture. And they're very smart people. Do you fancy the challenge?"

I told him that I did, that we should have the workshop in about a week's time, and I would provide everyone with a note of what to consider beforehand. I also showed Al the Double-E Double-A journey and told him that I would be using the workshop to help assemble the second stage, Explore.

"Will you be telling us about the first stage?" he asked.

"Yes, I'll share with you all the work I have just done with our friends in Australia. Do you know Craig, our CIO there?"

"No."

"You should, he's a great guy. Together with the CEO, he taught me a lot in a very short time. I'll put the two of you in touch."

We booked the workshop for Monday, the following week. Al thought this would give his people a chance to think about things over the weekend, if I could get the agenda to them by then.

After leaving him, I headed back to the elevators to see if I could have a quick conversation with Mrs. Zhang. As the doors opened, she was standing just inside! I told her I was just coming to see her for a five minute update, and to check something with her. She asked me to be as quick as I could, as she was headed for a meeting with the Finance Director.

"I'm hosting a workshop with Al and his team next Monday. I want to help them think about how they put the work they do into the context of the things that you and the other executives care about. Can I share with them the folder that you lent me earlier?"

"Yes, I want them to be much more interested in the commercial success of the company we all work for. If you can achieve that on Monday, I will be very happy. Please remind them that the information in that folder is privileged. They must not discuss or share it with anyone else, apart from the executive team."

"Can I email any of it to them, so that they can explore it over the weekend?"

"Which parts of it do you think would be most useful to them?"

"The headline ratios of the company's structural performance."

"I will send those to you electronically. Again, make sure they know that they are receiving privileged information."

"Of course, thank you."

"What do you think will be your most significant challenge?"

"Releasing them from some unhelpful constraints, both in terms of the scope they are working with and who they are looking to influence."

"I am certain you will be successful."

"Thank you."

We had arrived at an office which the sign on the door confirmed belonged to the Finance Director. Mrs. Zhang asked me to come in so that she could introduce me. "Good morning, Mr. Yao," she said. "This is Mr. Rathbone, from New York, who has joined us for a few days to help our Enterprise Architects enhance their contribution to our business success." It was a surprise to hear that I was from New York, as I still thought of my home as being in London.

"That will be a very valuable achievement," said Mr. Yao. "Thank you for coming."

"It is a pleasure to be here," I replied. "and a privilege to meet you."

With the introductions finished, I left Mr. Yao's office and went back downstairs to start preparing for the workshop. Just in case the EA team members had other plans for the weekend, I wanted to get the advance materials out to them by the end of Thursday, at the latest. Looking at my four subject headings for the Explore stage of EEAA (Stakeholders, Culture and Politics, Constraints, Architectural Themes), and given

Al's observation that the members of his team couldn't agree on one definition for EA, I decided to concentrate the workshop on exploring which constraints they considered to have the greatest impact on their ability to contribute to the company's commercial success. I also wanted to explore with them whether one of those constraints was the desire to have a single definition of EA.

I sent each of them the following instructions on what to do before the workshop and what to expect on that day:

Next Monday we are going to have a one-day workshop together on how Enterprise Architecture (EA) can grow its contribution to the company's success.

Attached to this email, as our context, are some of your company's key ratios relating to its structural performance. You must treat these as strictly confidential.

Please come prepared to answer two questions:

(a) In one sentence, what do you know EA to be?

(b) What are the five most significant constraints affecting the contribution of EA to the company's business results?

I need to stress that it is vital to the success of the day that you prepare, on your own, to answer these two questions. I expect that we will have a diversity of answers, which will be very valuable.

On Monday, we will spend the first part of the day exploring the work that I am doing with some of our businesses around the world. Then, we will turn our attention to the two questions above. Finally, we will summarize the actions you decide to take as a result of the workshop.

Please let me know if you have any questions. You can find me in Mrs. Zhang's department.

Regards,

Simon Rathbone

I knew that this might appear a bit vague to at least some of the people on Al's team, but I was ready to take the risk. I thought there was something appropriate about setting an open agenda for a workshop about constraints.

None of Al's team contacted me before the workshop, but somebody I wasn't expecting did. As I was sitting at the desk I was borrowing, a text came through on my mobile phone:

```
Bonjour Simon! Where are you
now, and when are you next in
Toronto? Francoise x
```

For a while, I just sat and stared at my phone, wondering what the text meant and how to reply. No solution came to me, so I stood up and walked over to the office windows, which faced the Bank of China Tower. Outside, there were, again, clouds among the buildings, softening the shapes of everything. Still not knowing what to do, I sent a neutral response:

```
Hello, Frankie. I'm in Hong
Kong, right now. Toronto is on
my schedule in a few weeks time.
Simon
```

The reply came almost immediately:

`Excellent! Let me know when.F xx`

To which I answered:

`OK, will do.`

Mrs. Zhang then interrupted my thoughts on what Frankie's texts might mean, by appearing at the window standing next to me.

"What do you make of the architecture here?" she asked.

"There is a lot of it in a very small space," was the best reply I could think of.

"Yes, that's true. Our Island is somewhat smaller than yours."

I looked at her, a bit puzzled as to which island she was referring to.

Seeming to read my mind she said, "Manhattan," and continued, "I am very interested to know what the Bank of China Tower, over there, reminds you of."

I looked at the building, thought for a while, and then answered truthfully, "I'm sorry, but I'm finding that a difficult question to answer."

"Thank you for your honesty. I understand it is designed on the theme of growing bamboo shoots, symbolizing livelihood and prosperity."

"That's very interesting. I think I can see the connection."

"I believe this is called 'structural expressionism'. It was also considered a controversial design, because of its sharp edges."

"Why does that make it controversial?"

"It was, I read, criticized by some practitioners of Feng Shui."

"Oh."

"As a kind of architect yourself, I expect you are familiar with how people express themselves through architecture, and how that may be controversial with others."

I began to realize where Mrs. Zhang might be taking this conversation.

I replied, "In Enterprise Architecture, I think there has been a tendency to think of standardization as the key to success. That may be at the expense of encouraging and valuing self-expression and local culture."

"Yes, I have noticed that. There is a delicate balance to strike between these things. I am sure you will bear that in mind for your workshop on Monday."

I said that I would, of course, bear it in mind. Mrs. Zhang left me to return to her office, and I sat back down at my desk to continue preparing for the workshop.

Here is how I ran the workshop with Al and his people.

For a start, I talked them through the short history of EEAA and what had happened in Australia. As we reached the subject of the Guiding Ratios, I reminded them of the ones that I had sent with the workshop agenda, and told them that we could expect to use different ratios for different businesses.

Then I moved on to the four elements of the Explore stage, on which I was now working.

For the first of these elements, Stakeholders, I said that the primary stakeholders in the enterprise's architecture were outside our business, in the market. In particular, we needed to be thinking about our customers and the experiences they had in which our enterprise and its architecture played a part. In response to this statement, a number of Al's team, and Al himself, looked uncomfortable, but said nothing. Two of the others smiled. I then said that, within a business, the executives are EA's primary stakeholders, rather than, for example, the people working in projects. This stirred up some more non-verbal reactions, but still nobody said anything.

I then moved on to the importance of Culture and Politics. As an example, I confided in them what had happened when I showed our Australian CEO some EA Guiding Ratios for his business that he did not know of himself. I said that I had taken this as a cautionary tale about considering the political and cultural impacts, before showing stakeholders our EA-related views of their world.

I then told them that, in their case, it seemed the story was more the other way around. Mrs. Zhang and the other executives in Hong Kong were concerned about the political and cultural impacts of showing their own EA-related views of the world to the EA team. More pointedly, they had noticed that doing this seemed to have no impact on the EA team at all.

Then, for the first time, one of Al's team spoke out by interrupting me with a question.

"I've never seen anything EA-related from the executives. What is Mrs. Zhang referring to?"

"For example, the performance ratios that I emailed to you all with the agenda for today."

"What have they got to do with EA?"

"They provide some vital context for deciding on the best contribution that EA can make to the company's performance. For Mrs. Zhang and the other executives - our primary stakeholders here - it is important that you make the connection in their minds between your business's structural performance, as illustrated by those ratios, and any work that you are doing for them, such as your Blueprints. Unless you can make those kinds of connections, the architectural designs and other artifacts you produce will lack real-world credibility, and your political and cultural influence will be very low." The person who had asked the question said nothing more, and nobody else picked up the thread, so I decided that would be a good place to end my story, and moved on to the practical part of the workshop.

For a start, I asked everyone to write down their one-sentence definition of EA on a piece of paper, and when everyone was ready, to place them all on the meeting room walls. No two definitions were the same, and not just in their wording. For some, EA was an activity, for others a framework, or a plan, or a team, or the actual architecture of the enterprise. About half of them mentioned technology, the others didn't. What surprised them was that I made no attempt to consolidate all of their definitions into one, or even a few, that we would all need to agree upon. Instead, I just said that the diversity of views was something that we should value and respect. Since they were all contributing to the architecture of the same enterprise, rather than agree on a 'perfect' definition of EA, as a team, they needed to commit themselves to having a unity of purpose. To help illustrate what I meant, I shared with them the work I had done with Matt and

Craig in Australia, which included the overall Promise that Craig had proposed for the generic Strategy for EA:

## Enhancing Enterprise Performance With Structural Innovations

This offered the Hong Kong team a potential unity of purpose. It also offered them an innovative and, for some, a controversial conclusion. We could each define EA as whatever we personally believed it to be, and put a high value on the diversity and self-expression this reflected. What mattered was that we were all working towards the same overall promise. I think a few of the group still wanted everyone to agree to their own definition of EA, or at least have a standard definition. But most were coming around to the view that having unity of purpose was a more feasible and worthwhile objective.

Then, for the Constraints, I instructed each of them to write their 'top five' on a new sheet of paper and place them on the walls. This time, however, I invited them to walk around the room for a while and explore all the statements now on view. If they didn't understand the meaning of anything they saw, they were to ask for clarification from the person who wrote it. After an uneasy start, this developed into a hum of conversation. When that began to tail off, I asked everyone to choose the most significant Constraint they had read, but ruled that no two people could choose the same one.

As there were eight people in the room, including me, we ended up with that many Constraints. In no particular order, here are the ones we chose:

- Executives do not understand the concept of architecture as it applies to enterprises.

- People think Enterprise Architecture is mainly about IT.

- We don't know if we are spending our time and energies on the most valuable contributions.

- People like to sub-optimize, which makes coherent architecture harder to achieve.

- Company politics.

- *Other people do not always understand what we are talking about.*

- *The connections between EA and business results are not obvious.*

- *We are uncertain of the value we contribute to the enterprise's performance.*

I thanked them for all their hard work and explained what the final part of this process would entail. For each of the Constraints, we would discuss and agree whether it was in our power to resolve or not, and, as a result, what they, as a team, could do next. Here is a summary of the actions on which we agreed:

- *Rethink the way we are articulating the concept of architecture, as it applies to enterprises. Use stakeholders' own models and metaphors as our foundation.*

- *Accept as a truth that, at least for now, people generally think EA is* mainly about IT. However, make sure that we behave in a way that will, in time, convince them that EA is primarily about enterprise.

- Establish some principles for how we decide to spend our time and energies, and make sure we are constantly applying those principles in practice.

- Accept that many people like to sub-optimize, and facilitate connections between them where this enhances their success. This may mean influencing how people's performance is measured and rewarded.

- Accept that politics are a normal part of company life and positively participate in them.

- Adjust the language we use to that of the person or audience with whom we are speaking.

- Model for ourselves the connection between formalized EA and business results, then share and test this model with business executives.

- Starting with the Promise of our strategy, design some new measures and metrics for us, as influential members of the enterprise's leadership community.

They had concluded that only one Constraint seemed out of their hands to resolve, which was that all around the world, EA was mainly thought of as being about IT. My final challenge to them was, since they already had at least one friend on the executive team who knew differently - whatever the rest of the world might think - they could build on this support and resolve that Constraint within the company.

None of them knew which executive I was talking about, and some were visibly shocked when I told them. It seems that they had been treating Mrs. Zhang as someone to be avoided because she always asked them such difficult questions.

"She certainly does!" I agreed.

Al came to me afterwards and said, magnanimously, that the workshop had been very valuable, although it had left some of the team a bit confused. I asked him whether they were, by any chance, the ones who wanted everyone to agree on a single definition for EA, but he didn't know for sure, so I left him to explore the question further if he saw any value in doing so. He thanked me for giving him a new foundation on which to build the business contribution of his EA team.

From the Explore stage of my EEAA journey, all that was left for me to consider was the question of 'Architectural Themes'. Mrs. Zhang had already given me a clue, in her observation about the Bank of China Tower, but with it came a new and tricky question. What was the overarching design theme of the architecture we wanted for our enterprise?

I spent my remaining hours in Hong Kong exploring this question. It took me right back to the time that Lucy had gotten me drunk before I went to Tokyo with Michael. She had told me that the previous CEO's strategy was focused on efficiency, whereas Michael was focused on productivity. Was it as simple as that? I didn't think so. 'Productivity' didn't express an inspiring architectural theme like 'growing bamboo shoots, symbolizing livelihood and prosperity'. In the end, I decided to call Michael and ask him. In reply, he asked me why I thought he had liked my idea, in Tokyo, of 'virtual hubs'. But he didn't wait for me to answer.

"As I think you know by now, my architectural orientation starts with our customers' life experiences and how our Brands, Service, Products and Services appear in them. I come at our enterprise outside-in. I don't want customers to know or care how we are structured - or even the extent to which we, as an organization, physically exist. As far as they are concerned, to borrow a metaphor from our friends in IT, everything else should be lost in the clouds. Remember the Ghostbusters fire station?"

"Yes, I do. Both of them. The outside and the inside were actually two fire stations a continent apart, but as the audience, we never knew nor cared. I get it now."

"Right. Good. So, in summary, our overarching design theme is about an orientation that starts with our customers' experiences, and in which we are a virtual enterprise. So, how is our 'virtual hubs' innovation coming along."

"I'm sorry Michael, I don't know."

There was a short silence. Then he said, quietly, with more impact than if he had shouted at me, "I do. Why don't you?"

"I didn't realize anything was happening with it, yet."

"I said I would commission someone to look into how they would work, and I have."

"Nobody has been in touch with me about it."

"And you agreed to track them down if you didn't hear anything. I did what I agreed to do. I was expecting you to do the same. Are you not interested in how your idea is going to become reality?"

"Yes, I am."

"Then why aren't you overseeing its success? You are an 'architect', aren't you, and this is one of your 'works'?"

"Yes, I am, and it is. Who did you ask to look into the virtual hubs?"

"A friend of yours, I think. In Canada. Said you had dinner together."

I was just about to interrupt and say "Frankie", when he said, "Ivan."

"Oh, OK. I'll talk to Ivan."

"Yes. Good. At least you didn't apologize. Where are you going next?"

"Paris."

"I love Paris. Make sure you visit the Pompidou Centre."

"Why?"

"You'll see. Call me when you're standing outside it."

"A mystery."

"Sure. Sometimes it's more fun that way."

## Observations

- A business's Guiding Ratios may show that the best contribution of EA is to protect and sustain the existing architecture.

- Who Enterprise Architects appear to treat as their primary stakeholders will affect the level of influence they have with business leaders.

- There needs to be an obvious line-of-sight between the business measures of success and any EA 'artifacts', such as blueprints.

- Enterprise Architecture is constantly looking for the optimal balance between diversity and standardization.

- Unity of purpose is more feasible and valuable than attempting to agree on a single definition for EA.

- The overarching design theme for your enterprise's architecture provides the inspiration and reference point for more detailed design and investment.

# TEN

# Paris, France

Two days later, standing outside the Centre Georges Pompidou in Beaubourg, Paris, I phoned Michael.

"What do you think of the architecture?" He asked.

"Interesting."

"You can do better than that. What shape is it?"

"A box."

"Ok, a bit simplistic but let's carry on. What do you see on the outside of the box?"

I had to look and think for a moment, then realized what Michael was getting me to observe. "OK, I get it."

"Go on."

"The services are on the outside of the structure, rather than the inside. That's why this building is so well known. I think the architect did something similar with the Lloyds Building in London."

"Indeed. Now, I love that building you're standing next to, but I'm not about to design an enterprise that way. As I said to you before you left Hong Kong, I want our enterprise to have an experiences-oriented, high-performing, virtual architecture…"

I interrupted, as I had at last caught his drift, "..and not a services-oriented one! That would be a very different architecture. Now I see why you told me to come here."

"Sure. Now we're getting fully tuned-in with each other on the overall architecture we're designing, and why. As long as we can get people actively applying those three themes in everything they do - experiences-orientation, high performance and a virtual

organization - we'll all create a fantastic enterprise!
Now, about our French subsidiary. Lucy's over in Paris
with them at the moment, so link up with her. She also
knows what I am about to tell you. We're in final
negotiations to buy our main competitor there, which
will approximately triple the local company's size.
There are no other bidders, so it's simply a question of
price. I'm optimistic that we'll get it, and probably
within the next couple of weeks. Only the local
President, Strategy Director and Finance Director know
the details. Lucy is helping them with the due diligence
on our target's technologies."

"What do you want me to do?"

"Nothing. Just be there. Work on our Double-E,
Double-A journey and keep Lucy company."

"OK."

I arranged to meet Lucy for dinner that evening.
She surprised me by suggesting a different place than I
predicted she would. She chose a Thai restaurant near
the Bastille. It was very different from the other Thai
restaurant I had visited with Craig in Sydney. This one,
part of a chain, seemed much more 'Thai-themed', with
orchids everywhere and a waterfall. I wasn't sure

which of the two styles I preferred, but I found the ambience, food and service at both restaurants equally enjoyable.

Lucy turned up in a bright red tee-shirt and black jeans. I was still in my suit.

"Hello, stranger," said Lucy.

"Hello, yourself."

"Fancy a drink?"

"Very funny. But yes, please, I do."

We ordered a bottle of French red wine. Lucy continued, "So, what have you been discovering on your travels?"

"It's a long story, already. But to begin with, I think I have discovered myself."

"That's good. You needed to."

"I know, and it's mainly thanks to you and Michael, but also to all the great people I've been working with."

"Michael's been keeping me updated with your progress. It seems you have at last helped him to articulate his main design theme for our company."

"At last? I thought he knew already."

"You underestimate your influence, Simon. Michael did have a sense of what he was trying to achieve, but until he started working with you he had been unable to express it even to himself, let alone the rest of us."

I said that I was flattered.

"At least you're not blushing."

But then I did, of course.

While I was working in our Paris office, I followed Michael's direction very carefully. Some people, understandably, wanted to know what I was doing there. I told them that I was just stopping off on the way through from Hong Kong to Toronto, using it as a base to work from for a few days. My answer didn't quite make sense, even to me, but nobody asked me to explain my presence any further.

The next stage in the EEAA journey was 'Activate'. I wondered why I had called it that, as everything that I had already done in Australia and Hong Kong was very active. What had I meant? Then I noticed that throughout the first two stages, I had been working in private with other 'enterprise architects'. Activating EA meant starting to take it public. The Explore stage crystallized the main design themes, but did not come up with any structural innovations or do any design. Now the journey could move on to designing the enterprise's architecture and activating that design around the company.

That got me thinking about how much EA-related work would always be going on out there in the enterprise, compared with the number of official Enterprise Architects we would ever have. I looked back at the list of Constraints that the Hong Kong workshop had concluded, and the one about time and energy caught my eye. With more EA-related opportunities than any number of Enterprise Architects could ever actively influence, every Enterprise Architect must be highly skilled at knowing when to 'play' and when to 'pass' on making a contribution. They would also need to have a very active and effective network, to stay constantly aware of all the opportunities to make a difference, and have as many options as possible for influencing events.

With all this in mind, I decided that the four elements of the "Activate" stage would be: Structural Innovations, Architecture Designs, Play or Pass, and the EA Network. I also marked the Private and Public split[3] on my overview of the EEAA journey:

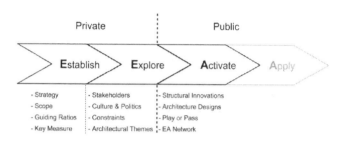

I showed this to Lucy, who, of course, had not seen any of it before. I told her that I had been assembling it by working with the people in Australia and Hong Kong. This was the first time I would be doing it on my own.

"Maybe not," she said, "I'm here. Can we do this one together?"

---

[3] Author's note: Private/Public victories – an echo of Stephen Covey. Are Simon's Establish-Explore-Activate-Apply stages 'the four habits of highly successful Enterprise Architects'?

"That would be much more effective than me doing it alone. Thanks for the offer."

"No problem. How about tomorrow? I'm tied up the rest of today. And let's do it at the hotel, not here. I'll need the change of scenery."

We worked all the next day in our hotel's bar, which overlooked the river Seine. It took me about three hours to explain to Lucy what the first two stages meant, how I had arrived at them, and with whom. I'm proud to say that she looked impressed with what I had achieved, so far.

Then we moved onto the latest stage, Activate, and the four elements I had chosen.

"What do you mean by 'Structural Innovations'?" Lucy asked.

"Well, first, architecture is about structure. If something is not impacting the enterprise's structure, we don't usually need to be involved."

"Ok, I think I agree with you. Why the specific focus on innovations?"

"Because we're interested in new ideas for enhancing our enterprise's structural performance – encouraging people to have them, and having some more of our own. Also, we need to be protecting that performance from new ideas that might damage it."

"Hold on a moment. I asked you about innovation and you talked about new ideas. Are you saying that they are the same thing?"

"Now that's a good challenge. On-and-off on my journey, people have been talking about innovations and I've been assuming, without thinking to check, that everyone is talking about the same thing. But now that you've pushed me to say what innovation means, I'm not even sure myself."

"Nor am I. Let's look it up on the Web and see what we find."

Lucy Googled 'innovation' and it came back with about 107 million hits. We clicked on a few and looked for anything resembling a definition. First, there was a distinction between innovation as a process and an innovation as the output of that process. All-in-all the consensus seemed to be that innovation means successfully exploiting new ideas (rather than having ideas or investing in those ideas), so we settled on that as our definition.

"So what do you define as 'structural innovation'?"

"The process of exploiting an idea that could materially affect the architecture of the enterprise. This includes ideas that are not directly about the architecture - such as a new product or service - but will need to affect the architecture, if they are going to be successful."

"That makes sense, in theory. Can you give me a practical example of a structural innovation?"

I told Lucy about the 'virtual hubs' idea.

"Oh, yes, the one Ivan is doing the designs for. He told me about it the other day. He's really excited, because it's helping him to break out of IT. He's working with some of the strategy people in NY and they've told him that if he mentions IT just once, they'll send him back to Canada!"

This was getting embarrassing. Was I the only one who did not know what was happening with my own architectural idea?

Lucy continued with a challenge. "But that's explicitly against changing the enterprise's structure. Doesn't that contradict your definition?"

"Depending on the design options that Ivan comes up with, I expect it will affect the way the structure behaves, even if it doesn't obviously change it in the way that something like a 'shared services' organization does. Anyway, I did say 'affect' not 'change'."

"Suitably pedantic. OK, you got me there."

I didn't like Lucy calling me pedantic,[4] and I told her so. "It wasn't meant to be an insult," she said, "although I can see why you might take it that way.

---

[4] An old EA joke:

A Project Manager and an Enterprise Architect are in a meeting. The Project Manager uses a word incorrectly, and the Enterprise Architect interrupts him to point out what the word really means. The Project Manager retorts in frustration "I'm fed up with your pendanticism," to which the Enterprise Architect replies, in a victorious tone of voice, "I think you'll find that it's pedantry."

Architects have to be pedantic about the details, when they matter."

"Fair point. I was also reflecting on whether we have exploited the 'virtual hubs' idea yet. Is it an innovation, or simply an idea?"

"What do you think?"

"Well, simply by mentioning it in Japan, I seemed to have influenced two very senior executives to think differently and act on those thoughts."

"Very true. If I turn that around the other way, they are already exploiting the idea in the context of their strategic thinking, and in what they are asking people to do. So it's already an innovation rather than just an idea. The design work that Ivan is doing is exploiting it further, and so on. No doubt he will come up with more ideas for us, and others, to exploit. The ultimate exploitation of your idea would be if we manage to turn it into value for our stakeholders, but meanwhile, that example alone shows how complex innovation can become, even if we only track the exploitation of one idea. Given how many people are having ideas and exploiting them in our enterprise alone, the daily challenge facing Enterprise Architects is where and when to make the most valuable interventions in a complex network of innovations that are going on all the time."

"Yes. I think that's where I was going with 'Play or Pass', which we're coming to next; although you've now articulated the reason in a way that I've never considered before."

"Great!" Lucy said, getting really quite excited, "Let's keep going, then."

Lucy and I had talked about Structural Innovations. To a small extent, we had also touched upon Architectural Designs, but without knowing how Ivan was doing with the only active design I was aware of, there wasn't much more I could say to Lucy on this subject. I will, however, come back to it later.

We moved on to 'Play or Pass'.

Lucy said, "I feel this is at the very heart of what it means to be a highly-valued architect. It's probably the most important element in the entire EEAA journey."

I asked her why she thought it was so important. She said, "Felt, not thought."

"Now who's being pedantic?"

"Absolutely," and we both laughed.

She continued on the subject of Play or Pass. "The reason I feel this is what EA is all about is because there's more Enterprise Architecture in the world than Enterprise Architects to do it. That conversation we just had about the complex landscape of innovations shows how many EA-related opportunities are constantly bubbling up everywhere, to which we have to add the ones that Enterprise Architects themselves create. The most important decision every Enterprise Architect has to keep making is which opportunities to play in - and how - and which to pass on. Either way, the decision will have an impact on what happens next."

I said that I had been having very similar thoughts. One of the main reasons for having everything that Matt, Craig and I had established in Australia, and that Al and his team had explored in Hong Kong, was to help Enterprise Architects make their Play or Pass decisions. Lucy looked back at the

Double-E Double-A process. "Strategy, Scope, Guiding Ratios, Key Measure, Stakeholders, Culture and Politics, Constraints and Architectural Themes. I agree. Without those eight things for a start, how can Enterprise Architects ever decide when to Play or Pass?"

"Indeed. Everything is now really starting to connect together."

"It sure is. How did you ever have the idea for EEAA in the first place?"

"It came out of thin air." I told her about my doodling on the flight back from Tokyo to New York.

"Literally thin air, in your case! Metaphorically, thin air is probably where many great innovations come from." Having made this observation, Lucy returned to Play or Pass. "As I said a moment ago, whether an Enterprise Architect plays or passes on an opportunity, the decision will have an impact on what happens next. So as time goes by, I think every Enterprise Architect would be wise to keep a log of the opportunities they knew about, what their decision was and why."

I agreed with her and sketched on a spreadsheet some examples of what an Enterprise Architect's 'Play-or-Pass Log' might include:

**Enterprise Architect's Play-or-Pass Log**

| Business Unit | Opportunity | Play or Pass? | Rationale for Decision |
|---|---|---|---|
| France | New Product Launch | Pass | No structural impact |
|  | Re-Organization | Play | May impact Guiding Ratios |
| USA | Business Acquisition | Play | Evaluate EA implications |
|  | Branding Review | Play | Cohesiveness with Service Experience |
|  | Boston Office Move | To Be Confirmed | Checking for any EA impacts |
| Australia | Processes Redesign | Play | Coalition with UK, Denmark, Singapore |
|  | New Service Principles | Play | Potential EA Innovation |
| Hong Kong | Technologies Upgrade | Pass | Sufficient Local Expertise |

Lucy said that looked like a great start. While I had been creating it, something else had crossed her mind. For the enterprise's architecture to achieve the CEO's design, there would need to be many more people than Enterprise Architects doing 'enterprise architecture'.

"That's where the final element of the Activate stage comes in, the EA Network. We have to have a network of people designing the details of the architecture, investing in bringing them to life and making sure they collectively achieve the CEO's design. I am getting very close to concluding that the reason we have Enterprise Architects is to activate and facilitate that network. I've just realized that this is what Michael has had me doing. With that network activated, Enterprise Architects constantly use 'Play or Pass' to choose why, when, where and how to influence the architectural decisions that people are making – whether those people know it or not – and how everyone acts on those decisions."

"So the EA Network in the Activate stage of the EEAA journey starts with the kinds of people you have been working with - the Global CEO, Business Unit Presidents and CEOs, CIOs, Commercial Directors, CFOs, CTOs, and so on?"

"Yes."

"That makes you a very influential person, Simon."

"I know."

"How do you feel about that?"

"How do I feel? Fantastic! And frightened."

"That's exactly how I would feel, if I were you."

I really enjoyed collaborating with Lucy in Paris. Although she was the person who had recruited me into the company, this was the first work we had actually done together.

After I left Paris, we bought our main competitor there. Lucy was asked to stay on as the new CTO, to merge the two companies' IT systems. Following a conversation with Michael, she agreed to do this as an interim role for six months, before handing it over to a permanent CTO and heading back home to America.

## Observations

- Establish-Explore-Activate-Apply: the 'four habits of highly successful Enterprise Architects'.

- Innovation: successfully exploiting new ideas.

- Enterprise Architects focus on structural innovations.

- Architecture is concerned with how a structure behaves, as well as the structure itself.

- The core skill of an Enterprise Architect is knowing when to 'play' and when to 'pass'.

- An enterprise's EA network starts with the senior business leaders.

# ELEVEN
## Abu Dhabi, UAE

The next stop on my travels was Abu Dhabi, in the United Arab Emirates, where we had recently made a significant investment in an up-and-coming business with high growth potential.

Just as I was leaving Paris, Michael's PA, Trudy, told me by email that he had instructed her to book me into a particular hotel. It was one that he had not yet been to, and he wanted me to tell him what it was like. "He says that you're to find the roof bar and tell him what you can see from there."

When I arrived, the taxi from the airport took me on a looping drive to the Yas Hotel, on Yas Island. I was amazed. Much of the structure was covered with what looked to me like a cloud-shaped web. It was dusk when I arrived, and from some distance away, I could see the entire shape lit up purple. Underneath the cloud, if that is indeed its theme, it turned out that the hotel is two buildings, each an elongated oval shape, one perpendicular to the other.

The hotel sits among a marina and a Formula One racing circuit. I say 'sits among' because the marina partly surrounds the hotel, and the racing circuit runs between its two buildings. The hotel has its own private bridge across the racetrack. In the bridge there is a bar. There is another bar up on the roof, under the 'cloud'.

I told Michael all of this, and I'm sure I could hear him smiling over the phone. "Which bar are you in?"

"The roof bar."

"What's its name?"

"What – the bar?"

"Yes."

I turned to the barman and asked what the bar's name was.

"The Skylite Bar."

"What can you see from where you are sitting?"

I wasn't sure what Michael wanted to know.

"Some tables, chairs, some large loungers with cushions…"

"Ok, what else?"

"The Formula One circuit – it passes right though the hotel you know - and the Marina."

"And?"

"And what?"

"Above you. The roof."

"What about the roof?"

"I want to know what the roof looks like, close up."

"It's a kind of metal webbing, curved, like clouds I think. Each individual aperture in the web has a metal grill set at an angle on the outside - hold on, is that to create shade? We're in the desert, of course, and shade is vital. And the whole structure is lit up purple on the outside with a light fixed at every intersection in the web."

"Sounds like an amazing structure."

"It is. Yes, it is."

"What do you think of the attention to detail, now that you're up close to the roof?"

"Once you know the big picture, the attention to detail makes the architecture what it is."

"Yes, that's what I think."

"But when I was in Sydney, I noticed that without first standing back from the architecture and appreciating its shape, the detail loses its meaning."

"Indeed."

"Apparently, a kind of architectural paradox. If you get too close to the details, you can't see the architecture, but architecture is all about the details."

"And, if we're talking about a building, what's the solution to that apparent paradox?"

"Start by standing far enough away from the building to appreciate its shape, its architectural themes and its place in the wider environment. Then you can get up close if you like, and go inside. I got that from Matt in Australia."

Then he surprised me by saying, "So did I." He left a short pause, and then continued, "Now, let's apply all that to the architecture of our enterprise, rather than a building."

I was becoming very certain that, as I had been touring the world, Michael had been guiding me through his approach to architecture, to develop our working relationship and my understanding of what he needed from me. A different CEO, in the same circumstances, would probably have planned some very different architectural experiences.

Michael knew that I had reached the final stage of the EEAA journey – Apply. Before I could think of the four elements that would make up that stage, he told me what he wanted them to be. These were the processes and experiences in which EA most needed to appear, so that the company's business units worldwide would be actively applying his design to their decisions and actions. Here is what he dictated to me - both the headings, and what they meant (as questions for people to explore and answer):

<u>Strategy Scenarios</u> - What are the implications for our enterprise's architecture, of alternative futures that might occur in the external environment, or of alternative strategies we might decide to pursue?

<u>Business Planning</u> - What structural innovations are most worth investing in to enhance our enterprise's architectural performance?

<u>Investments in Change</u> - What is the overall impact on our enterprise's architecture of all the changes we are investing in, plus those we are considering for investment?

_Enterprise Architecture Coalitions_ – How are our businesses working together to take full advantage of the architecture in which we have already invested and how are they investing in changing that architecture together, where that would be more beneficial than acting alone?

Michael's four elements made the EEAA journey complete:

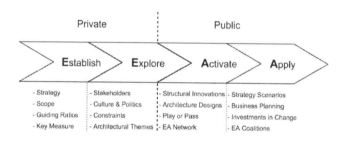

**"Double-E, Double-A"**

I asked him how I should apply those four elements in Abu Dhabi. He said that they would be a great proving ground as they were a relatively new business and not yet set in their ways. They were just at the point of exploring some strategy scenarios. The President, Mr. Abdulla Al-Khouri was expecting me.

Our Abu Dhabi offices were in the city center, about 30 minutes in a taxi from the hotel, overlooking the Corniche and the Gulf.

I was shown to the President's office, and we sat down in some very large, comfortable armchairs. I played with the thought of suggesting to Michael that he get some.

"Welcome to Abu Dhabi," said Mr. Al-Khouri, "It is good of you to come."

"It is an honor to meet you, Mr. Al-Khouri."

"Please, Simon, you must call me Abdullah."

"Thank you, Abdullah. I understand from Michael that you are looking at some strategy scenarios. Would you tell me about them, please?"

"Of course. We need you to help us."

Abdullah told me that they were considering three alternative scenarios for the Middle Eastern market and their strategy for growing the company there. There was also, of course, the de facto scenario. I asked him what that was, and he told me it was whatever the business would become if they just carried on as they were, operating the way that they did and investing in whatever changes they already had planned. "Unless we do something deliberately different," he said, "That is our as-is scenario, as I believe you Enterprise Architects like to call it."

"In fact," I replied, "that is indeed what an as-is scenario should always consist of, but often Enterprise Architects call today's enterprise the 'as-is', forgetting that there is also a plan for investing in change, which will happen 'as-is' unless a different plan is chosen."

"Interesting," observed Abdullah. "Now, what my managers and I need you to help us with – and please ask for whatever assistance you would like – are the high-level architectural implications of each strategy scenario. We know it is wise to take those implications into account when deciding how to proceed."

"How would you like those implications expressed?"

"Great question! I can see why Michael values you so much. I need you to help me and my executive team to understand and compare where, in the enterprise's architecture, we will most need to innovate, and where we will most need to invest."

"Do you anticipate that the answer to those two questions will be the same?"

"No, I think they may well be very different. They are a different kind of risk."

It was surprising, and thought-provoking, to hear Abdullah talking about both innovations and investments as risks, but I immediately saw his point. While they are both value-creating things to do, they don't always succeed and may destroy value in the process. So a strategy has to evaluate of the levels of risk that may impact its ability to succeed.

I told Abdullah that I envisaged a comparison table that articulated the enterprise's architecture in straightforward terms, and indicated, for each scenario, the levels of innovation and investment that would be required. He said that would be very valuable. "I will introduce you to my Enterprise Architect. He will assist you, and when you leave us he must know how to do this. We cannot keep relying on you for something we must be capable of ourselves, especially when you have the rest of the world to look after."

The Enterprise Architect, Jan van Veen, was from the Netherlands. After he and I reminisced about Amsterdam for a few minutes, I told him what Abdullah had asked us to do. Jan's problem was that although he was included in the group that was formulating the business's strategy, he was finding it difficult to express the architectural implications of the strategy scenarios in ways that the rest of the group could understand and then use in their decision-making. It seemed, I said, that Abdullah had now told me what they needed. Did Jan have a big-picture view of the enterprise's architecture?

"Yes, of course I do," he replied, with a serious look. (Had my question caused offense – I wasn't sure.) Jan continued, "People, Processes, Technologies."

This was a very familiar answer, and I thought about it for a while. I was remembering the journey I had been on, what I had learned and why Jan's approach might not resonate with executives.

"Can I suggest some changes?" I asked Jan.

"Go ahead."

"First, I think we should explicitly identify our enterprise's customers. Our business scenarios may require them to accept an innovation or make an investment, and if it does, then the level of risk will be much higher. That means we now have 'people' twice, so I think we should change 'people' to organization – which also makes it more structural. We're also missing our Brands, our Service, and the Products and Services that our customers buy. They are the reasons we need an organization, processes and technologies. And knowledge, of course."

Jan had been drawing while I had been talking. "So you are suggesting that we express it like this?" he asked, and he showed me the subjects I had covered as a stack of blocks:

| Customers |
|:---:|
| Brands |
| Service |
| Products & Services |
| Organization |
| Processes |
| Knowledge |
| Technologies |
| Partners & Suppliers |

I told Jan that I didn't think that a simple stack was the best way to express something as complex and multi-dimensional as an enterprise. Also, I remembered the principle that The Customer Has the Process - as well as access to knowledge and technologies - and therefore Jan's stack need re-sorting. I redrew it like this:

| Customers |
| --- |

| Processes | Knowledge |
| --- | --- |

| Technologies |
| --- |

| Brands | Service |
| --- | --- |

| Products & Services |
| --- |

| Organization |
| --- |

| Partners & Suppliers |
| --- |

Jan stared at my version of the stack for a few moments. He seemed to be coming to terms with something very significant, but I needed to see if I could draw him away from expressing the enterprise's architecture in this way. I quickly showed him the picture that I had developed with Matt and Craig in Australia, which illustrated the essentials of EA much better than a stack of blocks. And, following my conversation with Michael in Paris about his overarching theme for our enterprise's architecture, I could now give it a name – the Experiences-Oriented Virtual Enterprise:

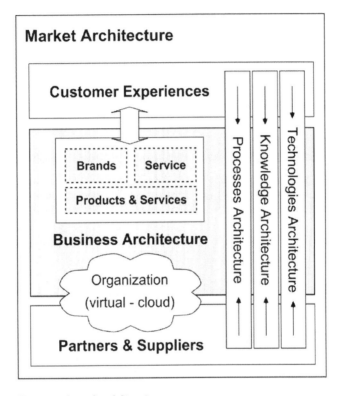

**Enterprise Architecture:**
**Experiences-Oriented Virtual Enterprise**

"So what you are saying," Jan observed, "is that customers have access to processes, knowledge and technologies with which to choose and experience our Brands, Service, and Products and Services.

Essentially, our organization exists to manage our Brands and Service, and to deliver Products and Services."

"Yes. And our customers should never know or care how our organization is structured. For all they know, it might not even exist. We should design the entire organization as a cloud."

"Wow! That's an amazing vision. And it really reflects today's world. How did you think of it?"

"I didn't. Our Corporate CEO in America did. This is his architecture for our enterprise."

Jan and I then spent five days together looking at the alternative strategy scenarios and the extent to which we thought they needed innovation and investment across the enterprise's architecture. We decided to define the possible levels of innovation as Breakthrough, Step Change, Incremental and None. The levels of investment we expressed as High, Medium, Low or None.

A couple of times we met with Abdullah to check that we were on the right track. Each time, he was very encouraging.

Our final table, despite being high-level, offered much for the strategy group to absorb, question and think about. When Jan and I had completed our work, Abdullah called the group together for a meeting. They concluded that some of our assessments needed changing, which we did. The table became known as the Portfolio of EA Scenarios. It looked like this:

## Portfolio of EA Scenarios

| | | Customers | Processes | Knowledge | Technologies | Brands | Service | Products & Services | Organization |
|---|---|---|---|---|---|---|---|---|---|
| As-Is Scenario | Innovation | None | Step Change | Incremental | Incremental | None | None | Incremental | Step Change |
| | Investment | Low | Low | Low | Medium | None | Low | Medium | Low |
| Alternative Scenario A | Innovation | Breakthrough | Step Change | Incremental | Step Change | Step Change | Breakthrough | Breakthrough | Incremental |
| | Investment | Medium | High | Low | Medium | High | Medium | Medium | Medium |
| Alternative Scenario B | Innovation | Incremental | Incremental | Step Change | Incremental | Breakthrough | Incremental | Step Change | Step Change |
| | Investment | High | Low | High | High | High | Medium | Low | High |
| Alternative Scenario C | Innovation | Incremental | Breakthrough | None | Breakthrough | Incremental | Incremental | None | None |
| | Investment | Low | High | None | High | Medium | High | None | None |

Abdullah and the strategy group took particular notice of the extent to which any of the scenarios depended on our customers innovating or investing. That, they agreed, would make a significant difference to a scenario's risk profile. It didn't mean they would avoid such scenarios, as they could be equally market-leading, but they would be especially careful in making sure that they succeeded and in managing the associated risks.

Michael's next context for applying EA was in Business Planning. Jan and I couldn't seem to make much of a connection between EA and the company's operational plans, so we focused on how to best apply EA in the business plans for investing in change. This is where it all had to come together. One of the strategic principles that Matt, Craig and I had concluded in Australia was:

*An enterprise's architecture is the aggregated output of all its investments in change*

If EA was not influencing people's plans for investing in change, then essentially it had no influence over the development of the enterprise's actual architecture. "I think the end-to-end process of investing in change is, itself, a vital part of our enterprise's architecture," Jan said. I agreed, so we decided to describe that process, the capabilities it needed for success, and articulate where EA needed to makes its highest contribution and have the most influence. Here is what we drew:

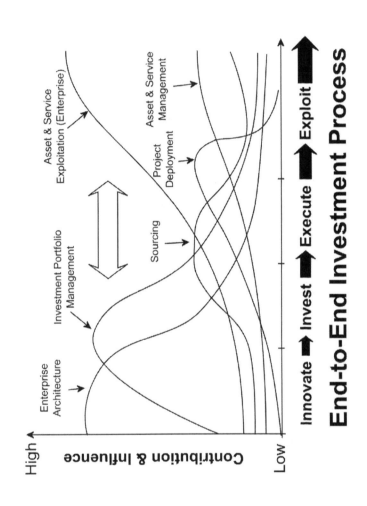

End-to-End Investment Process

This illustrated the strong interdependencies between the various capabilities that any enterprise needs, to be successful at investing in change. In particular, for the enterprise to be investing in the very best portfolio of changes, it needed to be highly effective in both Enterprise Architecture and Investment Portfolio Management. Then the process becomes about sourcing and deploying those changes. Finally, as well as managing the resulting assets and services, the enterprise needed to be capable of exploiting them to reap the maximum value. That last capability is, of course, the very essence of enterprise.

Jan and I also noted that the potential ability of an enterprise to exploit particular assets and services needed to be a major consideration in deciding whether to invest in them. So, as you can see, we inserted a large double-headed arrow to signify this.

Finally, Jan commented, "Most of the versions of this process that I've ever seen don't start with Innovate or end with Exploit. They tend to start with Initiate and end with Operate, or something like that. For Enterprise Architecture to really make the most contribution, waiting until something has been initiated is already too late. We need EA to be influencing people before they have even shaped an idea, let alone started to initiate an investment."

"You're right," I agreed. "And, if there's no Exploit at the end of the process, then we've lost the very essence of both innovation and enterprise."

Then we turned our attention to where EA is applied in the context of specific Investments in Change. We looked again at the End-to-End Investment Process and thought about how people decided on the architectural value of making an investment. Jan observed, "All the Investment Proposals, or Business Cases, that I have ever seen asked what the business benefits of an investment are going to be. None of them have asked about the contribution to the enterprise's architecture and its structural performance."

Once again, I agreed with Jan's insight, and continued the thought, "Then that is where EA must apply itself to investments in change. It must make the architectural value of a proposed investment be a vital factor in deciding whether to invest, and in the design of whatever changes are being invested in. It must be as important a question in every Investment Proposal as the specific business benefits of the investment.

We were nearly at the end of my EEAA journey. One last element remained: EA Coalitions. Jan and I talked about what we understood this to mean. We agreed it meant two or more people or businesses deciding to work together for both their individual and mutual benefit. It could take many forms, from two businesses simply sharing some knowledge, to a 'grand coalition' of all the businesses in a group sharing the capabilities they all needed, and perhaps commissioning someone to manage those capabilities for them.

From the perspective of being our up-and-coming Abu Dhabi business, this raised an interesting question: how many of the capabilities that this business would ever need were already in the rest of our businesses worldwide? What capabilities truly had to exist in the Abu Dhabi business itself? How virtual could we make it? Jan and I went back to Abdullah to talk this through with him. He was delighted, and told Jan that forming valuable coalitions with our other businesses around the world was an essential objective of his role.

"We are very happy to work with the other members of our corporate family, making investments together and creating the most value for all our customers, and for the corporation as our shareholder," Abdullah said. "However, we would be wise to recognize that businesses need local knowledge and relationships on matters that are important to the local market and culture."

"Thank you," I replied. "Then that is the model we will use."

In saying our goodbyes, Abdullah asked me whether I was interested in city planning, or just architecture. I asked him if he could clarify the reason for his question. "If you are interested in city planning, perhaps you could find time one day to take a look at the vision for our city's future, which is called Abu Dhabi 2030. It is driven and supported by our Urban Planning Council. I am sure you would find that you and they have much in common."

I thanked Abdullah for the recommendation, and for all the help that he had given me. "You are too kind, Simon. I think we have equally helped each other."

I took a taxi from our offices to the airport. As I sat in the lounge, waiting for my 14-hour flight to Toronto, I looked up "Abu Dhabi 2030" on the

Internet. I especially liked this description from the Urban Planning Council's website: "majestic in scope and delicate in its details." I felt that in eight words it articulated the very essence of Enterprise Architecture. I also noticed, from that same website, that Abu Dhabi is a carefully managed Brand, as well as being an Emirate. Fascinating!

I sent a text to Françoise saying that I was on my way home, via Toronto. I was getting quite excited about the prospect of seeing her again. By the time the plane took off, she had not replied. But, with an eight-hour time difference, it was, I realized, the middle of the night in Canada.

## Observations

- The solution to the apparent architectural paradox: first observe from a distance, then focus on the detail.

- Different CEOs have their own architectural metaphors, values and approaches.

- Enterprise Architecture must appear in, and influence, a business's own processes for strategy and planning.

- Enterprise Architects work with a portfolio of scenarios.

- The 'as is' scenario includes the existing plans for investing in change.

- An enterprise's architecture is multi-dimensional and complex.

- The end-to-end process for investing in change is a vital part of an enterprise's architecture.

- The process of investing in change starts with innovation and ends with exploitation.

- The design of a virtual enterprise starts by considering what must be local to each market.

# COMING HOME

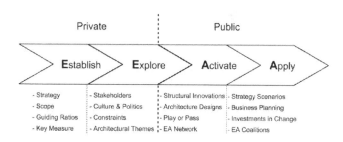

"Double-E, Double-A"

# TWELVE
## Toronto, Canada

Lucy had been right. Toronto felt very different, the second time. With my EEAA journey completed, I wondered why she had suggested I go there before heading back to New York. In the meantime, Ivan, himself, was in New York working for Michael on the design for the virtual enterprise; and I had received that cryptic text from Françoise.

I phoned Lucy in Paris and asked what I was doing in Canada. "I think someone is waiting for you there," she said. "Someone with a French name..." I could hear her smiling.

Then I called Michael and asked him to give me the background on our Canadian business. "Here are my instructions," he replied, sounding rather formal. Then he laughed. "Take a couple of days off. You've been on a long journey, and I keep hearing great things about you. Well done, my friend. But then I need to see you back here in New York to update me on what you've found, and tell me what I need to be doing next. See you in three days."

I noticed Michael had said that he wanted me to tell him what to do next, not the other way around. As always, he was choosing his words carefully, and I was sure it was not a slip of the tongue.

With two days in Toronto, and no work to do, I found the courage to call Françoise, and we met for a drink and dinner. On short notice, she managed to get approval for two day's vacation, so the next day, we went to Niagara Falls. Then, being late summer, we also spent a day on Toronto Island. I think that is the best place from which to see Toronto, with the CN Tower thrusting into the air, the city clustered at its feet and Lake Ontario calmly acting as a liquid plinth.

Françoise was happy just listening to me talk about where I had been, the people I had met and the things we had done. She said it was the life she had dreamed of when she had accepted her role. "I get to see other parts of Canada, which is nice, but I would love to travel further, work in different cultures and design more enterprises."

"For that, I think you have to make sure you work in a corporate role, and then be very determined to go where the work is, rather than stagnate in Head Office."

"Could I do that, do you think?"

"Yes. I think you can. Oh, and I feel you can, too."

She looked at me, slightly puzzled, with soft, brown eyes, and then relaxed into a smile.

"You were a good man before you left on your journey, and you are an even better man for the experience."

"I've only just begun. I'm not sure what will happen next."

"Do you think you will want to stay here in North America?"

"Hmm. You are a very perceptive lady. Do I not look at home here?"

"You look more at home than before, but in yourself, rather than in a particular place."

"Well, I'm loving working with Michael, with Lucy and with all the other fine people I have met."

I paused for breath before saying what I really wanted to say.

"And I'm loving, more than anything, just being here with you now."

"Moi aussi, Simon. Me, too."

On my last evening with Françoise in Toronto, before I flew back to New York, my old CIO, Ian Taylor, phoned me from London.

"I have an opportunity for you, if you would like it."

"Do you mean a job opportunity?"

"Yes, I do. Working for a good friend of mine who is the CIO at another worldwide company. She's looking for a Global Director of Enterprise Architecture. Back home, here in London. Are you interested?"

"Maybe. I've been traveling a lot, just recently, and I could do with a trip back to London. If I manage to secure a few days' vacation, can we meet up for dinner one evening?"

"Ha! You said vacation, not holiday. You must be settling in over there in America. And yes, dinner would be good."

"Thank you. I'll let you know for sure in the next few days."

"I'm looking forward to seeing you again, Simon. I'm dying to hear what you have been doing."

Although I did want to tell Ian all about my travels, I realized that much of what I had done was extremely confidential. If he asked me about it again, I would need to be very careful with how much – if anything – I told him.

But, apart from that note of caution, I really was looking forward to seeing Ian again, and maybe redeeming myself with him. But first, it was time to head home to New York City, and to my meeting with Michael.

## Observations

- An Enterprise Architect provides leadership to executives.

- In any enterprise with geographical spread, an Enterprise Architect must expect to travel often.

- Great Enterprise Architecture is a strategic differentiator, which means it must be kept confidential.

"So," said Michael, "Tell me about your journey."

"Which one? My world tour, or Double-E Double-A?"

"Well, not very long ago, you walked into my office and caused me to think differently about what I do. As an experienced CEO, that is a very rare thing, I can tell you. What I also noticed is that you did not seem to realize what you had done. For someone who calls themselves an 'architect', that is unforgiveable."

"I understand, I think, what you are asking me about my journey. Do I now know better what influence I have on people? I believe so, although I'm sure I still have much more to learn."

"So do I, Simon. We all do. But to do what your title says that you do, knowing the influence you have on people is the difference between success and failure. People have enterprise, and enterprises are made up of people."

"I know. I can see that now. But, as you noticed, there are many people who think Enterprise Architecture is about technologies, and processes, knowledge, things like that."

"I don't really care what anyone else thinks about Enterprise Architecture. And those are some of our valuable tools and building blocks. In Economics, they are forms of Capital – both tangible and intangible. Enterprise is something else. But now you are influencing the way in which CEOs, Company Presidents, Commercial Directors, CFOs, CIOs and CTOs think, feel, make decisions and act. If, out there, Enterprise Architecture was created as a capital-centric discipline, then here you have recreated it as an enterprise-centric one. How does your success here, so far, compare with whatever you did before?"

"In my last job, in England, I had a team of ten Enterprise Architects. Here I only have me. But already I have had successes here that I could only have dreamed of there."

"You have a bigger team here than you seem to realize."

"Why? I don't understand?"

"Already you have assembled a worldwide network of very senior and experienced enterprise architects, and you have only just started. And, Simon, I am honored to be a founding member of that team."

Michael said the last sentence with a bit of a flourish. It said something about the journey I had been on that I did not feel at all uneasy about what he had said.

He said that he had concluded why CEOs like him needed people like me. "Let me remind you of your title. You are our Vice-President of Enterprise Architecture. I've realized, as I have been following your journey, that this is different from being an Enterprise Architect."

I interrupted him. "Yes, when I was in Australia I figured out that the Chief Executive Officer is also the Chief Enterprise Architect. That led me to conclude that people like me are your 'assistant architects'."

"No, you are not. Ivan is currently one of those, which is why I've got him working on our design. We can also buy help from external Enterprise Architects whenever we need to, as part of our virtual organization. The challenge we may have is holding them to our objectives. Your role is different. I think you have noticed how many people across our businesses are working on individual aspects of the total architecture, whether they know it or not."

"Yes, and I've also noticed that very few of them are in roles called 'architect'"

"Correct. The great majority are executives, like me, and our managers. At the moment, most of us probably don't get the concept of architecture, as it applies to enterprises."

"Our EA team in Hong Kong identified that as the first major constraint on their success."

"Good. Did they figure out what that meant for their contribution to our business over there?"

"Not by the time I had left, no. I think I am only just realizing that now, myself."

"Go on, Simon."

"OK. I'm going to borrow what you said a moment ago. A role like mine is to provide leadership to business executives and managers on how to think, feel, decide and act cohesively as architects of our enterprise."

"Absolutely. You are leading our corporate strategy for Enterprise Architecture. How does that sound?"

"It sounds like exactly what you have had me doing for the last few weeks. And the EEAA journey is a kind of roadmap for that strategy."

"No, as you said, it's a journey, not a roadmap. And there are many ways of navigating that journey. The journey will be different every time. It's unlikely that everything you've identified will ever happen in exactly the sequence that you've shown. Much will depend on what is taking place in a particular part of the enterprise at any given time. It is best to achieve things that will get the green light today, rather than expect that they will always happen in the 'right' order."

"I know. But I used to think that doing things 'right' was the right way to do things."

"Now there's a conversation we could have forever. What does it mean to do EA 'right'? Let's not bother ourselves with that one. We have a business to run, architecture to invest in, and a performance that we've promised to deliver. That's enough for me."

He then asked me what he needed to do next to help everyone to continue along the journey we had started and that I was leading. I said, "We need to figure out what would encourage people in our different businesses to work in coalition with each other when it's to their mutual benefit. That's just not really part of our corporate culture at the moment, and our design depends upon it."

"Excellent observation. Although, once again, it hadn't occurred to me before. I have a tendency to think in terms of structure more than culture. My usual reaction would probably be to establish an Enterprise

Architecture Council, or something structural like that. Leave it with me to think about when I have a spare moment. That means it will probably be in the bath!"

I told him about the Urban Planning Council in Abu Dhabi that Abdullah had suggested I look at, and gave him the website address. "They are overseeing the delivery of a vision called Abu Dhabi 2030. It's an approved sub-Brand of Abu Dhabi itself."

"An architectural vision for our enterprise that's an approved sub-Brand of our MasterBrand; now you're talking my language!"

While he was thinking about the cultural implications of having an Enterprise Architecture Council, or something else, Michael asked me to spend some time with Ivan. He wanted me to observe the design work that Ivan was doing, and make recommendations that might increase the momentum and improve its success, as it seemed to have gotten a little quiet in recent days. I asked him if I could take a short vacation after that, as I had some unfinished business back in London.

"Sure, but don't be long. I need you here."

I sat down with Ivan to find out how far he had gotten with the design for our Experiences-Oriented, Virtual Enterprise.

"In truth, I'm struggling," he said, candidly. "I'm not sure where to start."

I recalled the conversation with Abdullah in Abu Dhabi. "How about starting with the capabilities that we must have in a local business? Once you've established those, then you can design how we make the rest into a virtual organization – a 'capabilities cloud', if you like."

"Thank you, I'll start there."

"Who are you working with?"

"In practice, nobody, yet. I wanted to develop a model first, to show people and get their input. Also, the strategists I'm supposed to be working with have told me that if I mention IT once, they will send me back to Canada. That's made me worried about talking to them, in case I slip up and I have to go home."

"Yes, Lucy told me about that, when I saw her in Paris. But I am one of Michael's strategists, and I think you did just mention it."

He looked a little worried, so I left a dramatic pause and then winked at him.

"Very funny," he said, and then started to smile.

"Your secret is safe with me. Have they told you why they don't want you to mention IT?"

"I think it's because they want me to leave the technology to one side and concentrate on the wider business, first. I also think they are worried that I'm a technology fanatic."

"Are you?"

"No, not at all. I enjoy solving big technical challenges in imaginative ways. I would rather those challenges were about the enterprise's architecture as a whole, rather than technology in particular. It's just that so far, the only place that we Enterprise Architects have been able to find a role has been in IT."

"Well, not any more. This is our big chance to recreate EA as an enterprise-centric rather than technology-centric profession, at least within this particular enterprise."

"Thank you. That's helping to inspire me. But how do I handle the fact that other people think I'm a technology-centric person?"

"Well, yes, that would be a good reason for them not wanting you to mention IT. The best thing I can suggest is that you very obviously mustn't behave as a technology-centric person, and show people what you really value in life. But I reckon there's another very different reason why the strategists are guiding you away from technology, which is not about you at all. Would you like to know what it is?"

"Yes, I would."

"Let me ask you something. How far into the future are you designing for?"

"At least five years, probably more like ten."

"So, tell me what technologies will be available in five-to-ten years' time."

"That's impossible to say. There are all sorts of potential scenarios for what could happen. Technology changes so fast."

I sat quietly and simply looked at Ivan. He looked back at me, nodded, and then winked. He had gotten his answer.

I suggested that he not worry about creating a model, as we already had one that should suffice as the foundation for more detailed design. To put it into context, I talked him through the EEAA journey, then showed him the EA Scope model that had emerged with Matt and Craig in Australia. I said it would be more valuable if he could exploit and test that model, rather than invest his time and energy in creating another one.

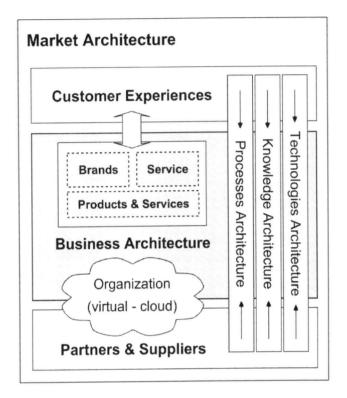

**Enterprise Architecture:**
**Experiences-Oriented Virtual Enterprise**

"Now, using this model," I asked him, "Who do you think it would be best for you to collaborate with on the design for Michael?"

His eyes moved around the diagram for a while and then he wrote some bullet points on his notepad. When he had finished he turned the pad to me and said, "These people. How am I doing?"

This was his list:

Brand Management

Marketing

Customer Service

Product Development

Human Resources

Sourcing

Process architects

Knowledge architects

Technology architects

Trusted partners and suppliers

I told Ivan that it looked like a good list to me and to get the collaboration going. I then asked him which of these people he saw as the best ones to approach first, given the kind of business we were in and the CEO's design for the enterprise's architecture.

"Brand Management."

"I agree. Who after that?"

"Customer Service."

"That sounds about right. Also, I am going to connect you with the people around the world that I have just been working with. Now, given your background and our earlier conversation, a significant question. When will you bring in the technology architects?"

"I would like to bring them into the process early, because technology is so integral to designing, changing and being an enterprise."

"But how would you explain that to your strategy friends around here?"

"If we are right about their reasons for banning me from mentioning IT, then there are a couple of things I would need to do. First, I need to make sure that whoever we ask to help with the technology aspects of our design are scenario thinkers. They have to know, like we do, that the further we look into the future with our design, the less we will know about the technologies that will exist. Second, we'll want people who can engineer technologies in new ways to meet our architectural design, rather than feel we have to be driven, or constrained, by whatever the technologists have already created."

"I agree. If architects allowed themselves to be constrained in that way, then some of the world's most inspirational buildings - and construction methods - would not exist. Are you comfortable telling that to the strategy people?"

"I think so. But can you come with me, in case I need support?"

"Yes, but I expect I'll just be decoration. I'm sure they will listen to your reasoning."

They did. And they agreed with him.

"But don't forget Michael," they warned him. "He is the chief architect of our enterprise, and this is his design we are all working on."

I left Ivan to continue his personal journey as our chief enterprise designer. Michael phoned me to say that he had decided to set up an Enterprise Architecture Council, along the lines of the Urban Planning Council in Abu Dhabi. He was determined, though, to make sure that council focused at least as much on the cultural implications of our strategy for Enterprise Architecture as the structural ones.

With Ivan and Michael working on the ideas I had given them, I headed across the Atlantic to London.

## Observations

- An experienced Enterprise Architect knows the impact they have on other people.

- There are two main 'schools' of Enterprise Architecture: capital-centric and enterprise-centric.

- Another way of interpreting these two 'schools' of EA is inside-out versus outside-in.

- The enterprise's senior management is the Enterprise Architect's primary team.

- An enterprise must know how to hold Enterprise Architects to the agreed design themes and performance objectives especially when working with partners and suppliers.

- EEAA is a journey, not a roadmap.

- The success of Enterprise Architecture depends on the enterprise's culture, as well as its structure.

- The longer the time horizon for an enterprise's architecture, the less it must assume about the technologies that may be available.

- The best people to be involved in designing an enterprise's architecture depends on the overarching design theme.

# FOURTEEN
## Home.....?

I grew up in London. For that reason, above all others, it will always be home. My mother still lived there, so I made sure I visited her as soon as I arrived.

"How are you getting on in America?" she asked.

"Just fine, Mother. Thank you for asking. The people there are very kind and they have just sent me on a journey that took me to Australia and back, via Hong Kong, Paris and Abu Dhabi."

"Have you met any nice young ladies?"

"Really, Mother! But, yes, I have met some nice young ladies."

"That's good. Why are you in London, apart from coming to see me, of course?"

"I am here to meet someone I used to work for. I think he has lined up a new job for me over here."

"That would be nice, Simon, to have you back home where I can see you more often."

Ian Taylor had arranged to meet me in, of all places, the Hard Rock Café near Hyde Park – the very one that my brother had taken me to as a teenager, when it had been the only one in the world.

"I thought you might feel at home," he joked loudly, over the music. "as you're almost an American."

"How are you doing, Ian?"

"Fantastic. Becoming the executive director of investments in change is what every CIO should aim for. How about you?"

"Very, very good, thank you. The last few months have been extraordinary and challenging. But

I've started to build a worldwide EA team and, as I told you on the phone, I'm working directly for the CEO. I am leading the corporate strategy for Enterprise Architecture, and it's a very different role than any I have had before."

"What's the biggest EA lesson you've learned so far?"

"The biggest EA lesson. Hmm. Good question. OK. Here goes. Business leaders have been the architects of their enterprise, whether they knew it or not, for as long as enterprises have existed. I've learned to call this 'informal EA'. About a quarter of a century ago, or thereabouts, a formal capability was born, called Enterprise Architecture. The mistake that I made, and I expect I was not alone, was to assume that this was an entirely new capability, and that I knew more than business leaders do about how to design an enterprise, bring that design to fruition and make sure that it worked in practice. The biggest lesson I have learned so far is that formalized EA, as it stands today, often has more to learn from business leaders about being the architect of an enterprise than vice-versa. The best strategy we can have for EA is to converge both informal and formal Enterprise Architecture in ways that enhance the actual performance of the enterprise. Any professionals in the still-emerging discipline of formalized EA who can successfully lead a strategy like that will, themselves, be regarded as business leaders. They are uniquely positioned to make an extraordinary contribution to their enterprise's architecture and performance."

Ian said, "Wow! Fascinating!" Then he changed the subject. "Don't you miss London?"

"Yes, I do." Before I could tell Ian that it was because London is where I grew up, and where my mother still lived, he carried on.

"Thought you would. So, as I mentioned the other day, I have an opportunity for you. Another CIO I used to work with is looking for a Global Director of Enterprise Architecture. You would be one of the CIO's five most senior managers and running a team of about twenty-five IT Architects. She would give you the freedom to design the IT Roadmap you've always dreamed of, with complete responsibility for making it happen. There may be some traveling involved, so it's good to hear that you're getting used to it, but much of the time you can probably work from their UK headquarters in West London, or even from home. How does that sound?"

"Can I think about it for a moment?"

"Of course."

My problem was not making the decision, but considering how best to express it. After a while, I said, "I feel, on balance, that I would be better off pursuing the role I now have over in the USA. I have just started to make an impact in the way that I want to and there's much more to do before I will be ready for the next challenge. I really do appreciate you thinking of me, though. Thank you."

"You're welcome, Simon. Do you know anyone else who might be interested?"

I thought of Françoise and our conversation about her desire to have a global role and travel more. But my loyalty to Michael, together with Françoise's value to our company (and to me) meant that I didn't think for very long.

"Unfortunately, not."

"OK. Well, it was good to see you again, Simon."

"You too, Ian. Let's stay in touch."

"That would be good. While you were thinking back there, I was starting to wonder what it would be like to team up again one day, to put your Strategy for Enterprise Architecture together with my Strategy for Investing in Change."

"Now there's a thought. Put the band back together again. Like the Blues Brothers. You and me - Jake and Elwood."

"That's good," he laughed, "I like it. Hopefully we would cause a bit less havoc than they did."

"Oh, I don't know, it could be fun."

"Fun. You never talked about having fun before. You've changed, Simon. For the better."

"Thank you. Coming from you, my friend, that means a lot."

"See you again, Simon."

"See you again, Ian."

After my dinner with Ian, I cut short my visit to London. I wanted to get back to North America, to Michael, Lucy, Ivan and Françoise, and all the other architects of our enterprise that I was beginning to collaborate with around the world.

There was no time to waste.

Because enterprises, unlike buildings, change their own architecture. To be a professional leader in Enterprise Architecture means first knowing that enterprising people make architectural choices whether you are there or not. It means offering guidance to the many people who invest themselves daily in changing the enterprise's architecture or keeping it the same; to facilitate structural innovations and new investment coalitions so that the enterprise, collectively, achieves the CEO's design.

There are so many opportunities for people like us to make an extraordinary contribution to an enterprise's performance. Our daily challenge is to figure out when to play and when to pass. And, in doing so, to follow the three golden rules that Michael offered me in the first few minutes that I met him: home is wherever the work is; there are never enough hours in the day; and many of the most senior people in an enterprise – whether they know it or not – are doing Enterprise Architecture. And in many cases, if not all, within their particular part of our business, they are doing it very well.

## Observations

- The best strategy for Enterprise Architecture is to converge both informal and formal EA in ways that enhance the enterprise's performance.

- Enterprises, unlike buildings, change their own architecture.

- For a professional Enterprise Architect, home is wherever the work is.

Made in the USA
Lexington, KY
14 October 2011